University Challenge Quiz Book

Independent Television Books/Arrow

University Challenge Quiz Book

Compiled by
Jean Sedley

Independent Television Books/Arrow

Jointly published by
INDEPENDENT TELEVISION BOOKS LTD
247 Tottenham Court Road, London W1P 0AU

and

ARROW BOOKS LTD
3 Fitzroy Square, London W1

An imprint of the Hutchinson Publishing Group

London Melbourne Sydney Auckland
Wellington Johannesburg and agencies
throughout the world

First published 1977
Reprinted 1978

ISBN: 0 09 915520 6

**Made and printed in Great Britain
by The Anchor Press Ltd
Tiptree, Essex**

Contents

Introduction

Granada Television's *University Challenge* has been entertaining British viewers since 1962. It is Britain's longest-running question-and-answer programme. There have now been thirteen series most of which have consisted of forty half-hour games.

University Challenge is a contest of general knowledge, coupled with quick thinking, played between teams of students from the universities and colleges of the United Kingdom and Eire. Quick thinking is essential because speed in signalling readiness to answer a question determines which player has the chance to do so.

Each team is made up of four people and the teams are chosen by the students of the college or university concerned. Each game is a head-to-head contest between the two teams. In the initial stages of each series the winners of each game go on to meet a challenge from a new team the following week. When a team wins three games in a row it qualifies to take part in a knock-out competition which concludes the series. The final of the knock-out competition is the best of three games and the winner is the champion.

How University Challenge *is played*

The game consists of starter and bonus questions. Starter questions are usually less difficult but require maximum speed in answering. They are worth ten points and may be answered by any of the eight players. In front of each player is a buzzer. The chairman begins to read out a starter. As soon as any player considers that he or she can answer it they interrupt by pressing their buzzer. Only that player may answer. If the answer is incorrect a penalty of five points is charged against the team and the rest of the question is given to the opposing team to answer. Once again only one player may opt to answer and there must be no conferring.

A correct answer to a starter earns the player's team a bonus question which normally has three or four parts and may have a value as high as forty points. All four members of a team may discuss the answer to a bonus question. In every game there is always a music or sound question and a picture question (not included in this book).

The winning team is the one with the most points when the game ends.

Over the years some 20,000 questions have been asked in *University Challenge.* For this book we have selected 875 of them, most of them arranged, starters and bonuses, as in the standard game covering a wide field of knowledge. But we have also added as a sort of additional bonus, some questions which are confined to specific subjects, so that you can play a *University Challenge* game about any of the following: Art and Architecture, Astronomy, Geography, History, Literature, Music, Mythology and Ancient History, Religions, Science, Sports and Pastimes, Theatre and Cinema.

From the very first *University Challenge* programme its chairman has been Bamber Gascoigne. He is well qualified for the job, for he has been at two universities himself: Cambridge (Magdalene College) and Yale in the USA. He was born in London in 1935 and while still at Cambridge began his association with show business at the A.D.C. Theatre in February 1957 as the author of a revue 'Share My Lettuce' which was later transferred to London and ran for over 300 performances. From 1961 to 1963 he was Drama Critic of the *Spectator* and in 1963-4 held the same post with the *Observer.* His interest in the theatre has resulted in two books: *Twentieth Century Drama* (1962) and *World Theatre: An Illustrated History* (1968). He has also written two novels, *Murgatreud's Empire* (1972) and *The Heyday* (1973), and a fable, *Ticker Khan* (1974). He has also collaborated with his wife, who is a professional photographer, to produce three books of history: *The Great Moghuls* (1971), *The Treasures and Dynasties of China* (1973) and *The Christians* (1977).

University Challenge was first produced by Barrie Heads with Peter Plummer as the director. For many years now the producer has been Douglas Terry and the director Peter Mullings.

GENERAL KNOWLEDGE 1

Starters

1. What is the precise meaning of 'corned' beef?
2. Who became Lord Cobham's gardener at Stowe in 1740, and was renowned for seeing the capabilities of the estates he was called on to improve?
3. What have Hamilcar Barca, Lord Kitchener and F D Millet in common?
4. On whose behalf did Siegfried woo and win Brunhild in the *Nibelungenlied*?
5. What ornament of medieval architecture derives its name from the French word for 'throat'?
6. Who wrote a systematic account of the methods of 'integration'—the beginnings of modern calculus?
7. In return for his services as prime minister how much salary does the prime minister receive?
8. What was the town on the Suez Canal which was built for the inauguration ceremony of the canal and was named after the then Khedive of Egypt?
9. From which vessel did Captain Briggs, his wife and daughter and crew apparently disembark somewhere in the Azores in December 1868?
10. Who started the two periodicals *All the Year Round* and *Household Words*?
11. In recent years when has Midas supplied answers to mysteries?
12. What is the name of the steak which comes from the undercut of the sirloin?
13. Who was the French naturalist who made a distinction between vertebrate and invertebrate animals?
14. In 1879 what name did the Cadbury Brothers give to their new model factory, which was situated four miles outside Birmingham?
15. What was the chief weapon of the German uhlan regiments?

Answers on page 78

Bonus

1. With which countries or peoples did these weapons originate?
   a) Kukri **b)** Kris **c)** Knobkerrie

2. In which capital cities are these famous gardens?
   a) Tivoli **b)** Heysel Park **c)** Vondelpark

3. **a)** From what is laver bread made? **b)** What is Kaffir bread? **c)** Which city lies on a bay in which stands the Sugar Loaf Mountain?

4. **a)** Who is commemorated by the Rodin sculpture which stands in the Boulevard Raspail in Paris? **b)** Which of Rodin's sculptures stands as the headstone to his grave? **c)** Which German poet was, for a time, Rodin's secretary?

5. **a)** What sect of the 16th century taught the doctrine of pacifism? **b)** What society which arose in the 17th century, has been closely associated with pacifism ever since? **c)** Which Anglican clergyman was one of the founders of the Peace Pledge Union in 1936?

6. **a)** What leaves were used for the wreaths worn by the victorious athletes of ancient Greece? **b)** An unbroken chain of what member of the Allium family could be worn as a protection against vampires? **c)** Which leaves adorn the coronets of dukes, marquises and earls?

7. On which day of the week are the following celebrated?
   a) Thanksgiving Day **b)** Ascension Day **c)** Budget Day

8. **a)** What is the name of Israel's parliament? **b)** Who was appointed UN mediator in the Arab—Israeli struggle of 1948? **c)** Who was the first president of the Provisional Council of the State of Israel?

9. From which language did these words come into English?
   a) Tabu **b)** Tattoo **c)** Tarot

10. **a)** For which queen did Josiah Wedgwood, in 1765, create a cream-coloured earthenware known as Queen's ware? **b)** What name did he give to his factory near Hanley? **c)** What was his relationship with Charles Darwin?

GENERAL KNOWLEDGE 2

Starters

1. Of what stone is nephrite one of the two only true varieties?
2. Which author wrote about St Ronan's Well in Innerleithen, Peeblesshire?
3. In which East German city did both Goethe and Schiller live for many years and then die?
4. What product is obtained from the plant *Camellia sinensis*?
5. In which Italian city is the ancient university whose nucleus is called 'Il Bo'?
6. Which Scotsman built the first railway in Africa?
7. Who made the first footprint on the moon?
8. What is the name of the television series in which the characters originally had the names of Pollux, Ambroise, Margot and Zebulan?
9. Who was responsible for the original design of the present St Peter's in Rome?
10. Which rare element lies between silicon and tin?
11. In which country did Shishak, the Great Chief of the Meshwesh, rule?
12. What was the name given to the international identity certificate which was created in 1922 for stateless persons?
13. What was the name of the Russian ambassador to Vienna in 1806, who commissioned Beethoven to write some string quartets?
14. What was Ebenezer Elliot describing in the early 19th century by the epigram, 'One who hath yearnings for equal division of unequal earnings'?
15. Which country, according to legend, connected Cornwall with the Scilly Isles?

Bonus

Answers on page 79

1. **a)** Who led the Barons in the 'Barons' War'? **b)** Which king was defeated by them at Lewes? **c)** In which battle was the leader killed?

2. Which four countries signed the Balkan Entente in 1934?

3. **a)** In which areas of the world did the apple tree originate? **b)** Which continent did dahlias come from? **c)** Which continent was the original home of freesias?

4. **a)** Which doctor died on the southern shore of the Bangweulu Lake in 1873? **b)** Which doctor died on the banks of the Ogowe river in 1965? **c)** Which doctor found himself an unintentional exile from his homeland in Africa in 1966, while he was visiting China?

5. **a)** What was the fatal weapon of the legendary animal, the basilisk or cockatrice? **b)** Which lover of his mother did Perseus turn to stone by showing him the Gorgon's head? **c)** In which state of the USA is the Petrified Forest National Park?

6. **a)** An estimated 45—47,000 men were killed between 15 and 18 June in one year in the 19th century. Where? **b)** An estimated 75—80,000 people died on 6 August in one year in the 20th century. Where? **c)** An estimated minimum of 68,596 died in one city in one year in the 17th century. Where?

7. **a)** Where are the Lindisfarne Gospels kept? **b)** Where can one half of the Lorsch Bible cover, an early ivory book cover, be seen in England? **c)** Where is the Book of Kells kept?

8. What line of business was followed by these famous families? **a)** Fries (Swedish) **b)** Fugger (German) **c)** Funk (American)

9. In which line of business did these millionaires make most of their money? **a)** John Davison Rockefeller **b)** George Peabody **c)** Ezra Cornell

10. **a)** What was bought for a mess of potage? **b)** What was sold to the US by Russia in 1867 for seven million dollars? **c)** What was given the hundred eyes of the giant Argus when the Argus died?

ART AND ARCHITECTURE

Starters

1. Which modern Romanian sculptor figured in a lawsuit in the USA against the US customs service?

2. What medieval treasure was acquired by the British Museum in 1946?

3. Who in 1883 decided to abandon his job in a stockbroking firm in Paris to be free to 'paint every day'?

4. What famous and controversial acquisition was made by Thomas Bruce, the third son of Charles Bruce, between 1803 and 1806?

5. Which city contains a famous half-completed church designed by the architect Antonio Gaudí?

6. Which architect built the famous church of Notre Dame du Haut at Ronchamp in France in 1955?

7. Who engraved in dry point *Christ healing the Sick* in a composition usually known as the 'Hundred Guilder' print?

8. Who designed the great window on the right of the main entrance of Coventry Cathedral?

9. Where is the group of statues called *Laocoon*?

10. Who was the first president of the Royal Academy?

11. Which architect called one house 'Fallingwater' and another 'Taliesin West'?

12. Who painted *The Burning Giraffe*?

13. Which American-born painter spent part of his boyhood in St Petersburg and later attended the Military Academy at West Point?

14. Who designed Balliol College, Oxford, St Chad's Church, Birmingham, and worked on the New Palace, Westminster?

15. Which painter had a grandson who advertised soap and who, though he ended life as an admiral, will always be far more famous as Bubbles?

Bonus

Answers on page 80

1. **a)** Which Spanish painter painted scenes in a 'madhouse'? **b)** Which French painter painted a series of five portraits of the insane in the Saltpetrière Hospital? **c)** Which painter spent a year, 1889-90, in an asylum at St Rémy de Provence?

2. **a)** In which country was the paleolithic figurine The Venus of Willendorf found? **b)** Who painted the Venus of Urbino? **c)** Who created the Cnidian Venus?

3. **a)** Who made the bronze statue of a condottiere which stands in a piazza in Padua? **b)** Which gilded equestrian statue stands in the Place des Pyramides in Paris? **c)** Which equestrian statue had the sitter's sword broken during an air raid on London during World War II?

4. Who painted the following well-known pictures?
   a) *The Pool* **b)** *The Avenue, Middleharnis* **c)** *The Reapers*

5. **a)** Who was the architect of the new Coventry Cathedral? **b)** Who designed the Regency terraces around Regent's Park? **c)** Who designed the Banqueting House in Whitehall?

6. Who painted these pictures?
   a) *The Naked Maja* **b)** *Resurrection, Cookham* **c)** *Third Class Railway Carriage*

7. Which Pre-Raphaelite painters created the following?
   a) *The Blind Girl* **b)** *The Hireling Shepherd* **c)** *Ecce Ancilla Domini*

8. **a)** For which monarch did Benvenuto Cellini make his famous silver and gold salt cellar? **b)** For whom did Leonardo da Vinci create *The Last Supper*? **c)** For whom did Fabergé create his famous imperial Easter eggs?

9. What were the Christian names of these artists?
   a) Poussin **b)** Maillol **c)** Modigliani

10. Whom do the following pictures represent?
    a) The Chandos portrait **b)** The Mona Lisa **c)** The Tragic Muse

GENERAL KNOWLEDGE 3

Starters

1. What class of vessel started with the *Warrior* in 1861 and ended with the *Vanguard* in 1946?
2. Who in 1886 said, 'All the world over, I will back the masses against the classes'?
3. What was the period of time shown by the sandglass in an 18th-century British ship?
4. Which soldier was in competition with Nasser for the leadership of Egypt after the 1952 military coup?
5. Which was the twentieth state to enter the USA?
6. For many years the mark was a unit of currency in England. How much was it worth?
7. What was the punishment of ostracism which was practised in Greece in the 5th century BC?
8. What are these? Dexter, Galloway, Red Poll, Brahman.
9. In which city did Sigmund Freud die in 1939?
10. Which English earldom belonged in turn to the family name of d'Aubigny, Radcliffe, Savile, Lennard and Yelverton?
11. Over what, at a meeting at Oxford in 1860, did T H Huxley have a disputation with Bishop Samuel Wilberforce?
12. What modern word in English or American derives originally from the ancient town in Bohemia called Jachymov or Joachimsthal?
13. What bulky form of transport was built at Friedrichshafen before World War II?
14. What Russian word was absorbed into English to describe the outbursts against the Jews which occurred between 1881 and 1914?
15. From which island in the Bay of Naples does the wine Epomeo come?

Bonus

Answers on page 81

1. What is the colour of these stones?
a) Porphyry **b)** Pentellic marble **c)** Lapis lazuli

2. Which is the odd man out in each of these three lists and why?
a) Symphonies: Borodin's Third, Schubert's Eighth, Bruckner's Seventh **b)** Plays: *The Father, Platonov, Uncle Vanya* **c)** Poems: *An Irish Airman Foresees his Death,* (W B Yeats); *ABC of Naval Trainee,* (Roy Fuller); *The Soldier* (Rupert Brooke)

3. In measuring weights the US and UK differ after 28 lbs.
a) How many lbs do the British gain in 1 cwt? **b)** How many lbs do the British gain in 1 ton? **c)** What do the Americans call a British ton?

4. **a)** Which capital city was founded as a capital in the 10th century by Jauhai al Rumi? **b)** Who was the first and greatest of the Ayyubid rulers? **c)** Which city joined Damascus as the joint capital of the Mameluke Empire?

5. **a)** Little Nell in Dickens' *Old Curiosity Shop* was based on his sister-in-law. Who was she? **b)** Who was the American girl who married Napoleon's brother, Jerome Bonaparte? **c)** Who was the sister-in-law of Charles II who later became Queen of England?

6. **(a)** What was the name of Svengali's famous pupil? **b)** Who was the famous pupil of William Grindell and Roger Ascham? **c)** Who was the famous pupil of Ann Mansfield Sullivan?

7. **a)** Who designed a Camel during World War I? **b)** Whose Aunt Dot rode on a camel to High Mass and took it to Trebizond? **c)** Who gave the camel his hump—according to Kipling?

8. **a)** Which American politician and backwoodsman was referred to as 'the gentleman from the cane'? **b)** In which war did he participate from 1813 to 1815? **c)** Who led the Mexican army at the battle of the Alamo?

9. **a)** Which poem begins with a triple repetition of a measurement which is equivalent to approximately 1½ miles? **b)** Who measured six cubits and a span? **c)** Which measurement was originally determined by the reach of outstretched arms?

ASTRONOMY

Starters

1. What is measured from a standard distance of 10 parsecs, to arrive at its absolute magnitude?

2. Which one of these signs of the Zodiac is the odd one out? Cancer, Aries, Pisces, Scorpio

3. Which Portuguese navigator is remembered in the two companion galactic systems to the Milky Way?

4. Who first described laws of planetary motion?

5. Which astronomer, physicist and mathematician discovered sunspots, mountains on the moon and the four moons of Jupiter?

6. In what year was the first artificial satellite put into orbit around the earth?

7. Who discovered the periodic variation in the brightness of the star Mira Ceti in 1596?

8. What part of a comet is the coma?

9. Where does the Bar shock wave occur?

10. Which planet is just visible to the naked eye only under favourable conditions?

11. What is Cassini's division?

12. Where in the solar system can Titan be found?

13. What is an aphelion?

14. What did Léon Foucault call the instrument he used in 1852 to demonstrate the rotation of the earth?

15. How long does it take for light to travel from the sun to the earth?

 Answers on page 82

1. **a)** What animal is chased by Taurus in the Zodiac? **b)** What great constellation contains Betelgeuse or Bellaxtrix? **c)** What animal's haunches are made up of the Plough?

2. **a)** Which lunar flight was struck by lightning? **b)** Which lunar flight was commanded by a 47-year-old grandfather? **c)** In which year did three American astronauts die in a flash fire while on ordinary routine tests on the launch pad?

3. **a)** Which are the inferior planets? **b)** Which is the planet nearest to the Earth but farther away than the Earth from the sun? **c)** Which planet has the largest diameter?

4. Which three constellations of the Zodiac are depicted as wholly human in form?

5. **a)** What is the name of the period of 6,585 days, after which an eclipse of the sun and moon recur? **b)** Who introduced Egyptian astronomy into Greece? **c)** Which Greek taught that the movement of the seven planets made the music of the spheres?

6. **a)** Whose tables of the moon's motion were first used in *The Nautical Almanac* in 1923? **b)** Whose experimental determinations in 1859 started the branch of astronomy known as astrophysics? **c)** What is photometry concerned with?

7. **a)** When will Halley's Comet next be seen? **b)** Which comet never properly appeared in 1974? **c)** At whose death are no comets seen?

8. **a)** Who started to develop the theory of radioactive equilibrium in 1916? **b)** Who first catalogued the dark patches in the Milky Way? **c)** Who has been called the 'father of modern astronomy'?

9. **a)** Which planet was discovered in 1781? **b)** Which planet was discovered in 1846? **c)** Which planet was discovered in 1930?

10. **a)** Into how many magnitudes were stars originally classified? **b)** Who started this classification? **c)** What is obtained by subtracting visual magnitude from photographic magnitude?

GENERAL KNOWLEDGE 4

Starters

1. The Romans had seven letters that represented quantities, e.g. X and V. What is the total if all seven are added together?
2. In about AD 435 who according to legend woke up from a long deep sleep and then died?
3. Who has a hook nose, a hunchback and a tendency to wife beating and child murder?
4. What was used by Sir Edward Henry to divide mankind into five basic groups?
5. In which trade or craft might a craftsman give his assistant a sequence of figures like the following (in inches)? 17, 31½; 8½; 20; 31; 40½; 35½; 42
6. Which animal has the male called a hob; the female, a gill; and the young, kittens?
7. Whose pace used to be slowed down by a second a week by putting an old penny on its works?
8. A famous American publication of the postwar period was the work of three authors. Two were Wardell B Pomeroy and Clyde E Martin. Who was the third?
9. Which language, still spoken in Britain, belongs to the Indo-Aryan languages?
10. What type of animal is a Galapagos Noddy?
11. Under what name is the flesh of the barracuda sold?
12. What is gossamer?
13. When was the International Labour Organisation first set up?
14. Which giant industrial company was born in 1903 and has grown in size ever since?
15. What did Gandhi mean by 'Swaraj'?

Bonus

Answers on page 83

1. **a)** Where, almost exclusively, are true lemurs found? **b)** Where do bush babies, a branch of the loris family, live? **c)** Where does the loris, or slender loris, live?

2. **a)** Which Florentine family had balls on a shield, usually seven, as its coat of arms? **b)** Which heraldic design is the badge of Florence? **c)** Who is the patron saint of the city?

3. **a)** Which body of people drafted the Westminster Confession? **b)** Whose were the *Confessions of an Opium-eater*? **c)** Whose autobiography in French was entitled *Confessions*?

4. **a)** Which garden lay on the other side of the brook Cedron? **b)** Which was the first 'Garden City' in Britain? **c)** Who painted the *Garden of Terrestrial Delights* as part of the triptych of Paradise, Earth and Hell?

5. Give the name for:
   a) The scientific study of the ancient life of the earth or its fossil remains **b)** The study of the constitution and properties of blood **c)** The study of projectiles

6. To which families do these birds belong?
   a) Ptarmigan **b)** Dotterel **c)** Ortolan

7. **a)** Which member of the camel family is indigenous to South America? **b)** How many humps has an Arabian camel? **c)** What is the name of the two-humped camel?

8. **a)** What are Hekla, Cotopaxi and Ruapehu? **b)** In which country is Timbuctoo? **c)** In which of the Soviet Socialist Republics is Samarkand?

9. In which fields did these people gain their fame?
   a) John Stanley Plaskett (died in 1941) **b)** Richard Cosway (died in 1821) **c)** Percivall Pott (died in 1788)

10. Which novelists created these characters?
    a) Widmerpool **b)** Scobie **c)** Somerset Lloyd-James

GENERAL KNOWLEDGE 5

Starters

1. Which Australian city stands on the Yarra river?
2. Which countess was the 'Darling Daisy' of Edward VII?
3. Which group of painters had a magazine called *The Germ*?
4. What did Master Jonathan Buttall become at the hands of Gainsborough?
5. How many times a day does the muezzin normally call?
6. Who invented the word 'galumphing'?
7. Which ruler made Peking the capital of the Mongol Empire in 1264?
8. What potent drink, basically a distillation of wine and wormwood, was prohibited in France in 1915?
9. What is the function of the hind legs of a cricket?
10. Which Scandinavian god obtained his supernatural powers from the possession of a hammer, iron gloves and a girdle?
11. Which explorer gained his objective in 1909, attended only by his negro aide Matthew Henson and four Eskimos?
12. Who defeated Admiral Sir Christopher Craddock at the battle of Coronel in 1914?
13. From the tower of which cathedral was Claude Follo thrown to his death by Quasimodo?
14. What title of rank lies between earl and baron?
15. In which field was François André Danican best known in the 18th century?

Bonus

Answers on page 84

1. **a)** From what illness did Walter Scott suffer when he was 18 months old? **b)** From what complaint did Dostoievsky suffer? **c)** With what physical impediment was Charles Dodgson afflicted?

2. Which is the largest island in each of these groups?
   a) The Orkneys **b)** The Canary Islands **c)** The Philippines

3. **a)** Who headed the coalition government of Britain at the outbreak of the Crimean War? **b)** Who headed the British coalition government of 1915? **c)** Who took over the leadership of the British coalition government in 1935?

4. Which of the United States of America are known by these popular names?
   a) Diamond State **b)** Equality State **c)** Flickertail State

5. **a)** What relation was Lot to Abraham? **b)** Who was the niece of Sir Toby Belch? **c)** What was the name of the niece and adopted daughter of the Peggottys?

6. **a)** Who was president of the United States at the outbreak of the Korean War? **b)** Who was the prime minister of Great Britain when the Boer War began? **c)** Who was the president of France at the outbreak of the Algerian War?

7. What were the subjects of the following amendments to the US Constitution?
   a) The fifth in 1791 **b)** The thirteenth in 1865 **c)** The eighteenth in 1919

8. **a)** What was bought for a shilling? **b)** Who were 'three-a-penny'? **c)** What were 'one-a-penny' or 'two-a-penny'?

9. What type of animals are the following?
   a) Monarch **b)** Dunlin **c)** Water moccasin

10. **a)** At which London hospital did Somerset Maugham study medicine? **b)** At which London hospital did John Keats study medicine? **c)** At which London hospital did Sir Roger Bannister study medicine?

GEOGRAPHY

Starters

1. What enters Lake Léman (Geneva) at Villeneuve and leaves it, then to pass through Geneva?
2. Where was the original Lusitania?
3. Which river rises in County Cavan and flows out into the Atlantic Ocean below Limerick?
4. In Chinese it's Kiang; in Mongolian, Gol or Song; in Japanese Gawa or Kawa; what is it in English?
5. Which island in Carmarthen Bay has been the intermittent home of religious groups for over 1300 years?
6. Which town lies between Milan and Turin and houses an ossuary which contains the bones of 9000 soldiers?
7. What important building stands on the most northerly point of the British Isles, being offshore from the island of Unst?
8. Which district of Cumbria is separated from Lancashire by the Duddon Estuary and Morecambe Bay?
9. What links the Isle of Portland to the mainland coast of Dorset?
10. In which island group is Gomera, whose inhabitants have a whistled language?
11. What name is given to the group of islands which contains Mauritius, Rodriguez and Réunion?
12. What did 'bradshawing' mean to early flyers?
13. Which Italian city is overlooked by the hills Valentino, Superga and La Maddalena?
14. Which is the deepest lake in the world?
15. Which is the highest capital city in the world?

Bonus

Answers on page 85

1. Which groups of islands include
a) Buka, Santa Ysabel, Guadalcanal **b)** Viti Levu, Vanua Levu, Koro **c)** Moorea and Tahiti

2. **a)** Which of the Great Lakes are linked by the Welland Canal? **b)** What is the unnavigable natural waterway link between these two lakes?

3. Manhattan is one of the five boroughs making up New York City—what are the other four?

4. Name the three major rivers which flow into the Baltic Sea?

5. What do the following names have in common?
a) Barton, Hickling, Ranworth, Filby **b)** Treek Cliff, Ingleborough, Speedwell, Wookey Hole **c)** Arden, Ashdown, Delamere, Dean

6. **a)** What is linked to the Sea of Azov by the Kerch Strait? **b)** What two waterways are linked by the Baghdad Railway? **c)** Which county is linked to Anglesey by the Menai Bridge?

7. **a)** On which river does Baghdad stand? **b)** Which city lies at the junction of the Blue and White Nile? **c)** Which city lies at the junction of the Avon and Wye rivers?

8. **a)** Which American state has the mockingbird and pecan tree as its symbols, friendship for its motto, and Lone Star for its nickname? **b)** Which state is known as America's icebox? **c)** Which is the 'Keystone' state?

9. **a)** Which river has the Irwell and Tame as tributaries? **b)** Which city is at the northern end of the Autostrada del Sole? **c)** The Kyle of Lochalsh is at the end of one branch of the road to where?

10. Kurds live in Iran, Iraq and which three other countries?

GENERAL KNOWLEDGE 6

Starters

1. What name did Israel Beer Josephat take after becoming a Christian in 1844?
2. Which large hoofed mammal occurs only in Africa and Asia?
3. In which calendar did the New Year date from 22 September?
4. What means of transport was used in World War I by the ICCB?
5. What plant was first cultivated for medicinal purposes in Banbury in 1777?
6. What name originated as a description of a certain section of New York and was later applied to the area around Denmark Street in London?
7. What name did James Herrington give to his Utopian version of England (the work was published in 1656)?
8. Which convent-bred girl confronted a political leader in the privacy of his bathroom to discuss revolutionary matters but instead brought the discussion to an abrupt end?
9. Which modern form of story-telling began in New York and Chicago newspapers at the turn of the century?
10. What is the familiar name for the fruit of the *Arachis hypogaea* which develops in a pod under the ground?
11. Which Spanish composer was drowned when the ship on which he was a passenger was torpedoed in 1916?
12. What, when it is an irregular shape, is called baroque?
13. Who first used the word 'commando' to describe military expeditions?
14. What by definition has a rectangular or square base, triangular sides and a pointed top?
15. What name is given to a peach with a smooth skin?

Bonus

Answers on page 86

1. Which writers created these detectives?
   a) Sergeant Cuff **b)** Father Brown **c)** Inspector Bucket

2. Which countries produce the following wines?
   a) Dao **b)** Barolo **c)** Franconia

3. **a)** Which is the largest peninsula in the world? **b)** Which is the largest bay in the world? **c)** Which is the longest strait in the world?

4. What are the names of the following lighthouses?
   a) On the Anglesey coast **b)** 12 miles south of Tiree **c)** 12 miles east of the mouth of the Firth of Tay

5. **a)** Which Gloucestershire doctor born in 1749 became famous for his investigations into the prevention of an infectious disease? **b)** Which Gloucestershire doctor was better known between 1865 and 1908 in the field of sport? **c)** Which Gloucestershire doctor died with R F Scott in 1912?

6. **a)** Which strip cartoon heroine had a dog called Count Fritz Von Pumpernickel? **b)** What is the name of Augusta's cat in the strip cartoon? **c)** What is the name of the hedgehog in the Hayseeds' strip cartoon?

7. Which US presidents were known as
   a) The Sage of Monticello **b)** The Rail-Splitter **c)** Old Hickory

8. In which countries or areas are watercourses which often dry up called
   a) Donga **b)** Nullah **c)** Wadi

9. **a)** What is a geophagist? **b)** What is a plantigrade? **c)** What is a pteridologist?

10. **a)** What is the well-known name for the Communist organisation which was founded in 1919 to foster the spread of world Communism, and was officially dissolved in 1943? **b)** What organisation set up in London in 1864 under the guidance of Marx and Engels became known as the First International? **c)** What is the shorter name given to the Communist agency which supplied information about the Communist parties of Eastern Europe from 1947 to 1956?

HISTORY 1

Starters

1. Who walked barefoot into a holy building undergoing a flogging because of his 'careless talk'?

2. Which of Louis XIV's ministers was responsible for the creation of the French navy in 1669?

3. In English law what year represents 'time immemorial'?

4. What was approved by Congress on 2 July 1776, although not made public for another two days?

5. In which city did Charlemagne build the Octagon, which was modelled on a church in Ravenna?

6. What public amenity is still colloquially attributed in Paris and Rome to the Emperor Vespasian who introduced it in Rome in AD 100?

7. What organised groups travelled through India in the first half of the 19th century garrotting people and stealing their belongings?

8. Who was hanged in Virginia in 1859, having been found guilty of murder, slave insurrection and treason against the Commonwealth?

9. What 14-year-old boy met a rebel leader at Smithfield in 1381 in an attempt to settle a revolt?

10. Where is a section of English history recorded on material, 231 feet long and 20 inches wide?

11. Whom did Pope Innocent III name as Archbishop of Canterbury in 1207?

12. Which Greek mathematician was killed by a Roman soldier during the siege of Syracuse?

13. After whose death did Abu Bakr become leader of his community?

14. Whose infamous reputation rests primarily on his actions following the Monmouth rebellion in 1685?

15. What was sold to France in 1768, just in time to make one of its greatest citizens a Frenchman?

Bonus

Answers on page 87

1. Which four great abbeys formed the 'Border' abbeys of the Norman period?

2. **a)** Which Portuguese explorer called the southernmost tip of Africa the Cape of Storms? **b)** Which king of Portugal changed its name to the Cape of Good Hope? **c)** Which Portuguese sailor first rounded it in 1497?

3. Name the fathers of these kings:
   a) George III **b)** Henry IV **c)** George I

4. Who held court at the following places?
   a) Cambaluc in 1271 **b)** Samarkand in 1400 **c)** Tenoch-titlan in 1520

5. **a)** Overlooking which important city is Bunker Hill? **b)** Who commanded the US forces after the battle of Bunker Hill **c)** Who was in charge of the British troops at Bunker Hill?

6. **a)** Who quarrelled with his royal patron and friend in 1812? **b)** Who found disfavour with his royal friend, despite his contention that 'if he banished him he might as well banish all the world'? **c)** Who lost royal favour in preference for Mrs Masham?

7. Of which countries did Napoleon make the following of his brothers, kings?
   a) Joseph **b)** Louis **c)** Jerome

8. **a)** What did Geoffrey, Count of Anjou, reputedly wear in his cap? **b)** What did the Mad Hatter wear in his hat? **c)** Which Roman Emperor, in his old age, never went out without wearing a petasus?

9. **a)** Who bestowed the title of 'Defender of the Faith' on Henry VIII? **b)** To which family did he belong? **c)** Which heretic did he excommunicate in 1521?

10. **a)** Who was the last king of Troy? **b)** Who was the last king of Portugal? **c)** Who was the last emperor of India?

GENERAL KNOWLEDGE 7

Starters

1. From which tree does the spice mace derive?
2. Of what are Grignard reagents, organic derivatives?
3. What was the position or function of the original tycoon?
4. What food was originally made from the dried meat of deer or bison?
5. What physical characteristic did Kipling's Shere Khan share with Tamburlaine the Great?
6. What is the name given to the French-speaking inhabitants of Belgium?
7. What was the name of the political party formed in Ireland in 1926 by Eamon de Valera?
8. Who was the first vice-president and then the second president of the United States?
9. Which husband and wife investigated the special properties of Joachimsthal pitchblende in 1898?
10. Which major dynasty ruled China between 1368 and 1644?
11. What name is given to a triangle which has sides measuring 5, 4 and 3 respectively?
12. Which English economist put forward the theory in 1798 that the population would increase more quickly than the food supply?
13. How many facets has a snowflake?
14. In which field of medical research did these three doctors, Carlos Finlay, Walter Reed, William Gorgas work?
15. Where are the Haversian canals?

Bonus

1. **a)** Which herb is known as the 'Herb of Grace'? **b)** How many 'days of grace' are allowed by law in England for the payment of a bill after the expiration of the time stated? **c)** The first issue of the British florin was in 1849. Why did this issue get the name of Graceless and Godless florin?

2. Which countries are the principal world producers of the following things?
a) Lapis lazuli **b)** Cobalt **c)** Uranium

3. Who wrote these 'prison' quotations?
a) 'For most men in a brazen prison live'
b) 'Shades of the prison-house begin to close
Upon the growing boy'
c) 'Stone walls do not a prison make,
Nor iron bars a cage;'

4. For what young kings did these people act as regent?
a) Edward Seymour, Duke of Somerset (under the name of Protector) **b)** Humphrey, Duke of Gloucester (under the name of Protector) **c)** William Marshall, Earl of Pembroke (under the title of *Rector regis et regni*)

5. What are the occupations or professions of these people?
a) Jean Brodie in *The Prime of Miss Jean Brodie* **b)** Ned Dennis in *Barnaby Rudge* **c)** Caleb Balderstone in *The Bride of Lammermoor*

6. **a)** Which famous eastern volcano erupted last in 1707? **b)** Which European volcano had a violent eruption in 1929? **c)** In which colony was there an eruption in 1961, from which the total population of the area was forced to flee?

7. **a)** Who was the possessor of a fatal handkerchief spotted with strawberries? **b)** Who washed Miss Lucy's three handkerchiefs, according to Beatrix Potter? **c)** Who 'held his handkerchief in front, so that the Carpenter couldn't count how many [oysters] he took'?

8. **a)** In which building was the famous 'Star Chamber' which in the 16th century came into use as a court? **b)** Who was chancellor between 1515 and 1529 when the Court of Star Chamber began to take its place as a regular part of the administration of justice? **c)** By an Act of which Parliament was it abolished?

GENERAL KNOWLEDGE 8

Starters

1. What was the Camorra?
2. Which is the only living bird which has two toes?
3. What is the connection between Lord Kitchener, a Lancashire Lad and a White Lion?
4. What is the technical term for long-sightedness?
5. What was worth a guinea a box?
6. What is anosmia?
7. Who holds the position of Admiral of the Port of London?
8. Who invented the wireless aerial?
9. What is the connection between Rhesus, Kell, Lutheran, Lewis and Abo?
10. What is the more common name of the 'Sword Lily'?
11. Which member of the Post Office surveying staff first suggested pillarboxes?
12. What does the word 'batrachian' mean?
13. For what are the following remembered? Hugh de Morville, William de Tracy, Reginald Fitzurse, Richard le Breton
14. With what is the study of helminthology connected?
15. What happened in England between 3 and 13 September 1752?

 Answers on page 89

1. **a)** Who was killed wearing a shirt smeared with the blood of Nessus? **b)** Who was killed wearing the armour of Achilles? **c)** Whom was Glauce about to marry when she put on poisoned garments given her by Medea and died?

2. Which armies were the main contestants in
a) The Seven Days' Battle **b)** The Seven Weeks' War **c)** The Seven Years' War

3. Who in the 19th century were nicknamed
a) Guy Vaux **b)** Silly Billy **c)** The Widow's Mite

4. **a)** Where did the Assyrians live? **b)** What was their capital? **c)** Which prophet ran away rather than preach repentance there?

5. In which countries or districts are the following regions?
a) Selvas **b)** Llanos **c)** Tundra

6. The following Latin names are all of common British members of the animal kingdom. What are their vernacular names?
a) *Lepus cuniculus* or *Oryctolagus cuniculus*
b) *Troglodites parvulus* or *Troglodites troglodites*
c) *Erithacus rubecula*

7. **a)** Which Tudor mansion was given to the nation for official use in 1917 by Lord and Lady Lee? **b)** Which former royal residence was presented to the nation by King Edward VII? **c)** To what official use is No. 12 Downing Street put?

8. Catherine de Medici had five sons, and the three eldest became successive kings of France. Who were they?

9. **a)** Which son of the vicar of Bishop's Stortford had a British territory named after him in 1885? **b)** The mining town which he went to in South Africa was named the following year after which Secretary of State for the Colonies? **c)** What was the name of the company he floated at Kimberley in 1880?

10. **a)** What does a wrongly tied reef knot become? **b)** What type of object is classified as a grandmother if she is no taller than 5 feet and no smaller than 2 feet 6 inches? **c)** What creature is sometimes known as Grandfather Greybeard?

HISTORY 2

Starters

1. What highly controversial office was held by these people? Victor IV, Pascal III, Calixtus III and Felix V

2. Whose fall in 1530 changed the name of York Place to Whitehall?

3. On what did the dog Nipper take the place of the recording angel at the turn of the century?

4. Which saint and Cappadocian father was the brother of St Gregory of Nyssa?

5. Who wrote the words 'Publish and be damned' when threatened by Harriet Wilson with the publication of his letters to her?

6. Where did the monks of Newbattle Abbey in East Lothian make salt?

7. Which Hindu custom was abolished in British India by Lord William Bentinck in 1829?

8. Where was the 'Instrument of Surrender' signed on 2 September 1945?

9. What was added to the US Army base about 35 miles south of Louisville in Kentucky in 1936?

10. In which war were members of the rifle clubs of France known as *francs-tireurs* first employed?

11. What famous 18th-century European king was called 'The Philosopher of Sans-Souci'?

12. What 'washing line' stretched in front of the Rhineland from 1936?

13. Whose diary was found in a tent on the Ross Barrier with its author and two other dead men in 1912?

14. Who followed Ferdinand and Isabella on the throne of Spain?

15. What was the better known name of the arbalest, a weapon of the Middle Ages?

 Answers on page 90

1. Two of the five people whom King Charles I sought in the House of Commons on 4 January 1642 were Pym and Hampden. Who were the others?

2. **a)** Which monarch made Leamington Spa royal? **b)** Who put the Regis in Bognor? **c)** Who made Tunbridge Wells royal?

3. **a)** Who led the Anti-Catholic riots in 1780? **b)** What nationwide movement led by Feargus O'Connor was responsible for various riots in 1839? **c)** Following the Riot Act of 1714 how many people were the minimum to constitute a riot?

4. **a)** From which city did the Borghese family originate? **b)** Whose brother-in-law did Camillo, 6th Prince Borghese, become in 1803? **c)** Who was the Borghese Pope?

5. **a)** What did Hogarth's Act protect? **b)** Whose laws consisted of the Law of Segregation and the Law of Independent Assortment? **c)** Which Act was introduced under Gladstone in 1873, and was accused of restricting English 'liberty'?

6. Which kings were killed in these battles?
a) Bosworth Field **b)** Flodden Field **c)** Senlac Hill

7. Who formed the triumvirate after the death of Julius Caesar?

8. In which wars did the following battles take place?
a) Matapan **b)** Bunker Hill **c)** Zama

9. **a)** When were traffic lights introduced into Great Britain? **b)** When were car registration plates introduced into Great Britain? **c)** In which year did the suffix 'A' come in for car registration?

10. **a)** What was the code name of the spy Jorge Antonio? **b)** Who was the chief organiser of British Intelligence under Queen Anne? **c)** What spy was appointed head of British Intelligence in liaison with the CIA in 1949?

GENERAL KNOWLEDGE 9

Starters

1. For what was Daniel Douglas Home well known in the 19th century?
2. What type of birds are called loons?
3. From which Greek word was 'gas' derived?
4. Whose ghost went round trying to sell *Cardium edule* and *Mytilus edulis*?
5. Who was the last king of England personally to lead his troops into battle?
6. What is normally mortgaged in a contract of 'bottomry'?
7. Where do you find together 'the Girdle of Venus', 'the Mount of Mercury', and the 'Via Lasciva'?
8. What is the more common name for the disease parotitis?
9. What is an 'alembic' used for?
10. To which group of gases do fluorine, chlorine and bromine belong?
11. Who was the first man to sail alone around the world?
12. What scheme of book classification is used in most libraries in Britain?
13. Who 'Lived in the Odium, Of having discovered Sodium'?
14. What relation was Stanley Baldwin to Rudyard Kipling?
15. Which English naturalist, born in 1627, was famous for his systems of natural classification?

 Answers on page 91

1. **a)** Who created 'Babar the Elephant'? **b)** Who included 'Baba the Turk' in an opera composed in 1951? **c)** Who translated *Ali Baba* into English in 1885?

2. **a)** Who restored her father-in-law Aeson to youth in Iokos by boiling him in a cauldron with magic herbs? **b)** In which idyllic valley did the chosen inhabitants live for 200 to 300 years? **c)** Who was restored to life after 100 years by Prince Florimond?

3. **a)** What is the name of the gulf on which Leningrad stands? **b)** On the delta leading to the shores of which sea does Astrakhan stand? **c)** What is the name of the sea on which Vladivostok stands?

4. **a)** Which town was the seat of government during Canute's reign? **b)** Which town was the capital of Mercia? **c)** Which Anglo-Saxon kingdom had a royal residence at Rendlesham?

5. Near which cities are these airports?
   a) Tempelhof **b)** Dum Dum **c)** Kastrup

6. What are the three meanings of the word 'Morse'?

7. In which counties are these National Trust properties?
   a) Glastonbury Tor **b)** Penshaw Monument **c)** The Dodman

8. What are the names of the following temples?
   a) The first of the three temples at Jerusalem **b)** The temple to the Egyptian god at Karnak **c)** The Buddhist temple at Kandy in Sri Lanka

9. What characteristic is implied if someone is called the following?
   a) A Benjamin **b)** A Benedick **c)** A Jonah

10. **a)** What is sometimes known as 'The Way of St John'? **b)** In what 'Way' does the Pontifex family feature? **c)** In what 'Way' does Mirabell love Millamant?

LITERATURE 1

Starters

1. Who stood on a London bridge, early one morning in September 1802, and watched the sunrise with inspired satisfaction?

2. Who had already been retired from the Belgian police force for sixteen years when he first appeared in 1920, but was still working in the 1970s at the apparent age of 130?

3. What was the name or profession of the 'wall' which separated two lovers who appeared before Theseus and Hippolyta?

4. Whose death inspired the poem, 'Break, break, break, On thy cold grey stones, O sea'?

5. Which American poet made a translation of Dante's *Divine Comedy* in 1861?

6. Who was preferred to W M Thackeray as an illustrator when the suicide of Robert Seymour put the continuation of Pickwick in jeopardy?

7. What name is given to a verse whose last foot is truncated, or even cut off completely?

8. Who visited Florence in 1860 and was there inspired to write a novel about Savonarola?

9. Who received a cravat for an 'unbirthday present' which Alice mistook for a belt?

10. In which town was the American author Nathaniel Hawthorne born?

11. Which of the six Brontë children survived their father?

12. Which famous collection of stories first appeared in Paris in 1704 in a translation by Antoine Galland?

13. Which fictional character was the heroine of *Silk Stockings*?

14. Which French writer's autobiography appeared in three volumes called *Memoirs of a Dutiful Daughter, The Prime of Life,* and *The Force of Circumstance*?

15. What was the name of the anxious parent in *The Tale of Samuel Whiskers*?

Bonus

Answers on page 92

1. **a)** Who lived at Manor Farm, Dingley Dell? **b)** What was the name of the inn where Mr Pickwick stayed when the action of Bardell *v* Pickwick was pending? **b)** Where was the parliamentary election held which Pickwick attended?

2. Which European authors wrote these modern versions of themes used by Sophocles?
   a) *Antigone* (1942) **b)** *Electra* (1903) **c)** *Oedipus Rex* (1928)

3. What are the last lines of the poems which begin
   a) 'I had a penny, a bright new penny' **b)** 'I wandered lonely as a cloud' **c)** 'If I should die, think only this of me'

4. Who was
   a) The Jew of Malta? **b)** Nobody in *The Diary of a Nobody*? **c)** Le Malade Imaginaire?

5. **a)** What was the name of Bill Sykes' lady friend? **b)** Who was the beloved of Don Quixote? **c)** Which 19th-century book tells of the love of Gerard for Margaret Brandt?

6. **a)** Who said, 'We are so very 'umble'? **b)** Which author created something nasty in the woodshed? **c)** Who 'took great Care of his Mother Though he was only three'?

7. What was the name of
   a) The Lady of Shalott **b)** The 'Lady of Christ's College' **c)** The Lady of the Chair in the Heavens

8. **a)** What characteristic did Swift's Struldbrugs possess which made them very miserable? **b)** Which immortal loved Psyche? **c)** Which immortal stole a boy from an Indian king and made her husband jealous?

9. **a)** Who intended to go to the Bell at Edmonton to celebrate his wedding? **b)** What detained the guest who rose 'a sadder and a wiser man' the next day? **c)** Who went to his wedding in 'irreverent robes' justifying it by saying that his wife was marrying him and not his clothes?

GENERAL KNOWLEDGE 10

Starters

1. What is Angus Smith's solution used for?
2. Who commanded Napoleon's cavalry at Marengo, Friedland and Jena?
3. Where does the word 'calculus' come from?
4. Where was Lawrence of Arabia born?
5. What is a 'spotted Irish lord'?
6. Who said in August 1914, 'The lamps are going out all over Europe; we shall not see them lit again in our lifetime'?
7. When were sleeping cars first introduced on railways in Britain?
8. Of what are the following a part? Poleyn, couter, pouldron, vambrace, greave and gorget
9. What is the Parisian connection between George V, Victor Hugo, Franklin D Roosevelt, Pasteur and Anatole France?
10. What was the last pitched battle to be fought on English soil?
11. Which country did Henry Cromwell rule during his father's Protectorate?
12. Which Labour politician was the son of a sister of Beatrice Webb?
13. Which New World animal has a scent-gland opening on the ridge of its back?
14. Who described Turkey as 'the sick man of Europe'?
15. What is the official name of the genus of conifers which includes the 'redwood'?

Bonus

Answers on page 93

1. By what names are the following people better known?
   a) Novelist N S Norway **b)** Novelist A H Hawkins **c)** Painter R H van Rijn

2. **a)** Which river was described as 'Grey, green, greasy'? **b)** Who first wrote, 'Sweet Thames run softly till I end my song?' **c)** Which river ran 'Through caverns measureless to man'?

3. Which three novels, together with *Rogue Herries*, make up the *Herries Chronicle* by Sir Hugh Walpole?

4. **a)** What relation was George II to George III? **b)** What relation was Queen Victoria to George III? **c)** What relation was George IV to William IV?

5. What are the French, German and Italian words for 'bat' (the flying animal)?

6. How did these characters die?
   a) Cordelia **b)** Juliet **c)** Emilia

7. What countries are the setting for these films?
   a) *The Overlanders* **b)** *The Seventh Dawn* **c)** *The Good Earth*

8. **a)** What did Shaw claim to be 'The greatest of evils, the worst of crimes'? **b)** What did Henry Stimson class as 'the only deadly sin'? **c)** What is proverbially 'a great traveller'?

9. Before British Railways what were the colours of the passenger carriages of
   a) Great Western Railway **b)** Southern Railway **c)** London, Midland & Scottish Railway?

10. **a)** In which country is the Lion's Rock (the ruin of a 5th-century AD stronghold)? **b)** What is the name of the natural hill fortress on the Dead Sea? **c)** By what name are the stone ruins, associated with the Shona people, known?

GENERAL KNOWLEDGE 11

Starters

1. Who wrote the *Vailima Letters*?
2. Who shared the Nobel prize for physics in 1909 with Karl Brown?
3. Which official is responsible for maintaining order in the House of Lords?
4. What plant is the principal food of the Koala bear?
5. What name was given to the laws, established by two acts in 1799 and 1800, which made trade unions illegal?
6. What is the usual colour for the textile 'bombazine'?
7. What is the only known infection which affects only the eye?
8. Which castle was built by Cormac McCarthy in County Cork in 1446?
9. Over which tribunal did Lord Justice Sir Geoffrey Lawrence preside?
10. Which Australian flew across the Pacific in 1928?
11. Who, in 1785, started the *Daily Universal Register,* which was renamed *The Times* in 1788?
12. What is the modern name for the Cretan port of Candia?
13. Of what material are the finest pearls composed?
14. Who accompanied John Jeffries on the first aerial crossing of the English Channel on 7 January 1785?
15. What discovery did W H Perkin make in 1856?

 Answers on page 94

1. What are the names given to the following geographical phenomena?
a) The belt of calms and light airs which border the northern edge of the NE trade winds **b)** The warm dry west wind which blows down the eastern slopes of the Rocky Mountains **c)** The dry warm wind in the valleys of the Alps

2. **a)** What smuggler captain had a cave on the shores of Wigtown Bay? **b)** In which book does he figure? **c)** Who is the gypsy woman in the story?

3. Who was the father of the following?
a) Charles Darnay **b)** Siegmund and Sieglinde **c)** Charlemagne

4. Which countries are connected by the following mountain passes?
a) Roncesvalles **b)** Brenner **c)** Kalgan Gateway

5. Which three knights in Malory find the Holy Grail?

6. Who are the three pyramids of Gizeh named after?

7. What are these people's full names?
a) Little Nell **b)** 'Pip' in *Great Expectations* **c)** Little Dorrit

8. **a)** What was the middle name of the author of *Under Milk Wood*? **b)** Whose middle name was Babington? **c)** Whose middle name was Love?

9. **a)** What was the Man of Spy? **b)** What animal is known as 'the man of the woods'? **c)** Who, in Puritan usage, was referred to as 'the man of sin'?

10. **a)** Fleance was the son of the Thane of Lochaber. Who was the Thane of Lochaber? **b)** Who was Edward Murdstone's stepson? **c)** Who was the father of George Washington?

LITERATURE 2

Starters

1. Who lent his grey mare to eight people to take them to a Devon fair?

2. For which battle was the lament *Flowers of the Forest* written?

3. Who is alleged to have said on his deathbed, 'Ring down the curtain, the farce is over'?

4. Whose fictional characters met regularly in Mindy's Restaurant?

5. To be taken off active flying service you have to apply on the grounds you are insane; but anyone who applies to be taken off active flying service is clearly not insane. What is this a definition of?

6. How was the Menai Bridge to be kept from rusting, according to a knight?

7. Who wrote *Prelude to Bolshevism* and *The Crucifixion of Liberty*?

8. What is the name given to the unrhymed measure which Henry Howard, Earl of Surrey, introduced into England?

9. What have these writers in common? Maurice Maeterlinck, Georges Simenon, Hugo Claus and Michael de Guelderode

10. Which French writer owed part of his success to the support of Madame Armande Caillavet?

11. Who was the British poet born in Shropshire and killed on 4 November 1918?

12. Which famous French poet wrote, it is believed, all his published poetry between the ages of fifteen and twenty-one?

13. What word links the titles of books by Philip Stubbes, Robert Burton and Anthony Sampson?

14. Who described Oxford as 'sweet city with her dreaming spires'?

15. Which poet called a cat the 'Napoleon of Crime'?

Bonus

Answers on page 95

1. **a)** Whose books tell the saga of the Irish Jewish family 'Glass'? **b)** Whose works tell of the life of Lewis Eliot? **c)** Whose work tells the story of Tevye?

2. What day of the week is associated with the following? **a)** A well-known work by G K Chesterton about a group of anarchists **b)** A detective from the American TV series *Dragnet* **c)** The proprietor of Eric Linklater's Poets' Pub

3. **a)** Whom did Humbert Humbert especially love? **b)** Whom did Lady Chatterley love? **c)** Whom did the fair Rosalind love?

4. What are the usual English titles of the three books of Sartre's trilogy *The Roads to Freedom*?

5. What three authors would be involved in **a)** a 'Boyfriend' meeting **b)** a 'Girlfriend' **c)** becoming an 'Ideal Husband'

6. **a)** In which country did the religious sect called the 'Little Endians' live? **b)** Who was the 'foxhunting London grocer'? **c)** Who were the original 'Baker Street irregulars'?

7. What was the name of **a)** The Warden **b)** The 'Leviathan' of Hobbes's treatise on political philosophy **c)** The Last of the Tribunes

8. **a)** Which 19th-century novel is subtitled *A Novel Without a Hero*? **b)** Which novel by Mrs Gaskell was subtitled *A Tale of Manchester Life*? **c)** Which novel by Lewis Wallace was subtitled *A Tale of the Christ*?

9. **a)** Whose last sonnet said, 'Bright star! would I were steadfast as thou art'? **b)** Whose love sonnet said, 'If thou must love me, let it be for naught/Except for love's sake only'? **c)** Whose love sonnet addressed someone as 'More lovely and more temperate' than a summer's day?

10. **a)** Who dwelt among the untrodden ways beside the springs of Dove? **b)** Who was asleep by the murmuring (Afton) stream? **c)** Whose father made cabbage nets and mother made laces?

GENERAL KNOWLEDGE 12

Starters

1. Who won the VC whilst serving in HMS *Chester* during the battle of Jutland?
2. What famous doctor was a cousin of Jean Paul Sartre?
3. What is the basic difference between a top hat and an opera hat?
4. In which language did these words originate? Lemon, cipher, sherbet, sofa, coffee
5. How was the phrase 'Mr Watson, come here, I want you' made famous on 10 March 1876?
6. What was the name of the Protestant statement compiled by Melanchthon in 1530?
7. Which French scientist, with his brother, was responsible for the development of cinematography?
8. Which philosopher propounded the theory 'He who knows Nature, knows God'?
9. Which was the first English daily paper (it started in 1702)?
10. What does the Japanese word 'Tsunami' mean?
11. What was the name of Hannibal's brother-in-law?
12. What do Scots call St Sylvester's Night?
13. At what time is the canonical hour of compline?
14. What does the word 'cuneiform' mean?
15. Who wanted to know where the snows of yesteryear had gone?

Bonus

Answers on page 96

1. Reynard is the name of the fox. What animals are called **a)** Chanticleer **b)** Isengrim **c)** Grymbert

2. **a)** How many Dalmatians were there in the film made by Disney? **b)** How many characters were searching for an author? **c)** How many made up Mary McCarthy's 'Group'?

3. Which American cities have the following names, when literally translated?
a) The Poplars, New Mexico **b)** Yellow, Texas **c)** The Plains, Nevada

4. These films are remakes. Name the original titles.
a) *Move Over Darling* **b)** *High Society* **c)** *Storm over the Nile*

5. What are the better-known names of these places?
a) Baile Atha Cliath **b)** Abertawe **c)** Kérkira

6. In which plays do the following characters appear?
a) Roebuck Ramsden **b)** Beattie Bryant **c)** Big Daddy

7. In which settings were these people assassinated?
a) Holofernes (killed by Judith) **b)** Archduke Sergei (killed by Russian revolutionaries in 1905) **c)** The Minotaur (killed by Theseus)

8. What was the stage name of **a)** Phoebe Anne Mozee? **b)** Matilda Wood? **c)** Harold MacLennan?

9. What numbers form part of the titles of these films?
a) *Fahrenheit* **b)** *Butterfield* **c)** *Boccaccio*

10. Which men held the office of British Foreign Secretary between October 1951 and 1 January 1960?

MUSIC 1

Starters

1. What is the name of the ability possessed by certain people to sing any note asked for?
2. Who composed the ballet suite *Corroboree*?
3. What was the original name of the Arts Council of Great Britain?
4. What is an autoharp?
5. How many Brandenburg Concertos are there?
6. Who was appointed professor at the Budapest Conservatoire in 1907?
7. Who was the first graduate in music of Trinity College, Dublin?
8. Who was organist at St George's Hall, Liverpool, from 1855 to 1894?
9. What was the basic dance form of the Black Bottom?
10. What is the Boehm system?
11. When was *La Bohème* first produced?
12. Which is the only wind instrument which is acoustically perfect?
13. How many demi-semiquavers are there in four crotchets and three minims?
14. Who wrote the song 'Hearts of Oak'?
15. To which Hungarian family was Haydn a Kapellmeister for thirty years?

Bonus

Answers on page 97

1. a) Of what organ family is the Mustel organ a member? b) Of which family is the flageolet a member? c) Of which family is the mandora a member?

2. a) When was *Ariadne auf Naxos* first produced? b) Where? c) Who composed it?

3. a) Who wrote a setting of 'Ring out Wild Bells' for a male voice choir and the Bournville Carillon in 1924? b) What have Wagner's *Parsifal*, Handel's *Saul* and Bach's cantata *Schlage doch* in common? c) How many changes are there in a ring of five bells?

4. Name any three of the 'Group of Five'?

5. Who are the composers of the following symphonies? a) The *Rhenish* b) The *Reformation* c) The *Resurrection*

6. Which countries have the following national anthems? a) 'The Emperor's Hymn' b) 'La Brabançonne' c) 'A Soldier's Song'

7. a) Who wrote incidental music to *Pelléas and Mélisande*? b) Who wrote an opera about Pelléas and Mélisande? c) Who wrote a symphonic poem about Pelléas and Mélisande?

8. Which three composers have written operas based on the story of Manon Lescaut?

9. a) What is the best material for making bells? b) What material was used to make a coach horn? c) Of what material was the musical instrument 'the serpent' made?

10. a) Who composed 'Ol' Man River'? b) Who composed 'Ol' Black Joe'? c) Who composed 'I've Got Plenty of Nuttin' '?

GENERAL KNOWLEDGE 13

Starters

1. Where is King Arthur supposed to be buried?
2. When does a banshee howl?
3. Who said, 'God will pardon me. It is His trade'?
4. What was an aepyornis?
5. Who wrote: 'Disinterested intellectual curiosity is the life blood of real civilisation'?
6. What is ichnology?
7. What is the unique significance of the Ahmes papyrus written thirty-five centuries ago?
8. In which battle were the Roman infantry legions finally crushed by cavalry?
9. Who first introduced the philosophy of pessimism?
10. Where did Handel's *Messiah* have its first performance?
11. Which Polish-born dancer and teacher was chosen by Diaghilev and Nijinsky to assist them in the original production of *The Rite of Spring*?
12. To what do the following names refer? Bodoni, Gill Sans, Bembo, Perpetua, Plantin and Times
13. Who wrote *The Uncommercial Traveller*?
14. Who was Helen of Troy's half-sister?
15. Which playwright wrote musical criticism under the name of Corno di Bassetto?

Bonus

Answers on page 98

1. **a)** What play was based on Henry James's novel *Washington Square*? **b)** In which of his stories does the heroine Millie Theale appear? **c)** On which of his stories was the film *The Innocents* based?

2. Which three countries celebrate their national days within seventeen days of each other in July?

3. **a)** Name the basilica which stands above the harbour of Marseilles. **b)** Name the cathedral in Prague which contains the body of Good King Wenceslas. **c)** Name the cathedral which stands in Moscow's Red Square.

4. What are the last lines of the sonnets which begin **a)** 'Much have I travelled in the realms of gold' **b)** 'When I consider how my light is spent' **c)** 'I met a traveller from an antique land'

5. Whose mother was **a)** Agrippina **b)** Given forty whacks **c)** Necessity

6. **a)** Who led the last completely successful invasion of Britain? **b)** Where did he and his army land? **c)** What year was it?

7. Who said **a)** 'Man is by nature a political animal' **b)** 'Man is by constitution a religious animal' **c)** 'Man is a social animal'

8. What were the previous names of these African countries? **a)** Ghana **b)** Malawi **c)** Zambia

9. Which kings of England had the following nicknames? **a)** Beauclerc **b)** Lackland **c)** Yea-and-Nay

10. Who wrote the following plays? **a)** *One More River* **b)** *Two for the Seesaw* **c)** *Ane Satyre of the Thrie Estaites*

GENERAL KNOWLEDGE 14

Starters

1. What peculiarity have Old London Bridge, the 18th-century bridge over the Avon at Bath and the Ponte Vecchio in common?

2. Name the most decorated American serviceman of World War II who later became a film star?

3. Of which Greek dramatist did Aristophanes say, 'Gentle he was in life, gentle in the life beyond'?

4. The Greeks called dawn Eos; what did the Romans call it?

5. Which character in a Thomas Hardy novel sold his wife and child for five guineas?

6. Who was king of England when Greenwich Observatory was founded?

7. Which Greek philosopher is sometimes known as the Stagyrite?

8. Where would you find a Pale, a Chief and a Bar?

9. What does the Solvey process manufacture?

10. In which building was King Charles I tried?

11. Who is taunted by the frogs in Aristophanes' comedy *The Frogs*?

12. Which 19th-century Prime Minister was responsible for passing the Artisans' Dwelling Act and the Sale of Food and Drugs Act?

13. Who was acclaimed as the returning God-King Quetzalcoatl, when he arrived from the east in the year prophesied by Aztec legend?

14. What small British falcon shares its name with a legendary magician?

15. What is the common name for the plant *Geranium sanguineum*?

Bonus

Answers on page 99

1. Who were the husbands of these ladies?
   a) Andromache **b)** Helen **c)** Hecuba

2. **a)** What is the army equivalent to a naval lieutenant? **b)** What is the naval equivalent to an air vice-marshal? **c)** What is the WRNS equivalent of a group captain?

3. What is a tropical storm called in the following places?
   a) The Caribbean **b)** The Indian Ocean **c)** The China Seas

4. **a)** Which children's book is based on a game of chess? **b)** Which ballet, first performed in 1937, is based on a game of chess? **c)** In which film made in 1956 does a knight play chess with Death?

5. In which groups of islands are the following islands?
   a) Grenada **b)** Hoy **c)** Herm

6. On which rivers do these cities stand?
   a) Berlin **b)** Montevideo **c)** Benares

7. **a)** Which actress had Sir Hugo de Bathe as her second husband? **b)** Which widow had Henry VIII as her third husband? **c)** Which film actress had, as her third husband, the late Ali Khan?

8. Who were the authors of the books on which Bizet based these operas?
   a) *The Fair Maid of Perth* **b)** *L'Arlesienne* **c)** *Carmen*

9. What were the titles of the three 'Unpleasant Plays' in G B Shaw's *Plays, Pleasant and Unpleasant?*

10. In which cities are these famous museums and art galleries?
    a) Fitzwilliam Museum **b)** The Hermitage
    c) Rijksmuseum

MUSIC 2

Starters

1. Who wrote the words of these three hymns? 'All things bright and beautiful'; 'Once in Royal David's City'; and 'There is a green hill far away'
2. To which composer did Mozart dedicate his Quartet No 19 in C Major?
3. To which god in particular were 'Paeans'—songs of triumph—originally sung?
4. Whom did Franz von Walsegg's servant visit to ask him to compose a Requiem Mass in 1791?
5. What does 'Con sordino' mean?
6. Which composer's grandfather emigrated from Scotland after the defeat of Culloden?
7. What was the original nationality of Rudolph Friml?
8. Who is the Swiss composer of the orchestral work, which is a football tone-poem, called 'Rugby'?
9. On which building in Rome does the last act of Puccini's opera *Tosca* take place?
10. Who wrote the music for the ballet *Les Biches*?
11. Which is the Gilbert and Sullivan opera which satirises the aestheticism of Oscar Wilde's era?
12. Who wrote the 'Marseillaise'?
13. Which French composer studied medicine before studying music?
14. What was the title of Béla Bartók's only opera?
15. Which Czech composer spent five years as director of music at Gothenburg in Sweden?

Bonus

Answers on page 100

1. Who composed the following symphonies?
   a) The 'Drum-Roll' **b)** The 'Haffner' **c)** The 'Israel'

2. **a)** What is the name of a guitar-shaped six-string cello? **b)** What is the name of a Hungarian instrument of the dulcimer type played with sticks? **c)** What is the name of a small harpsichord with one keyboard, and one string to each note?

3. **a)** Who arranged Bach's music into a ballet suite called *The Wise Virgins*? **b)** Whose music was used for the ballet *Good Humoured Ladies*? **c)** Whose music was used for the ballet *Pineapple Poll*?

4. **a)** Which British composer used the colours purple, red, blue and green to describe the movements of his 'Colour Symphony' in 1922? **b)** Which opera did he compose to a libretto by J B Priestley? **c)** Which ballet set in Scotland did he complete in 1944?

5. **a)** Which composer, whose father was West African, wrote *Symphonic Variations on an African Air*? **b)** Which opera has an Ethiopian princess as its heroine? **c)** Who composed an opera based on Othello seventy years before Verdi?

6. **a)** For what did Walter Von Stolzing win a prize in opera? **b)** By what means did Max win the contest and his bride in Weber's opera *Der Freischutz*? **c)** In which opera did Don Alfonso win a bet by proving the faithlessness of women?

7. Who composed these choral works?
   a) *The Nelson Mass* **b)** *Belshazzar's Feast* **c)** *Judas Maccabeus*

8. **a)** What animal's name is sometimes given to Haydn's Symphony No 82 in C? **b)** Whose so-called 'Sonata' for harpsichord is sometimes nicknamed the 'Cat Fugue'? **c)** Which composer wrote a work which has been nicknamed the 'Dog Waltz'?

9. **a)** Who first asked, 'Has anybody here seen Kelly'? **b)** For which masque/oratorio did Handel write, 'Where e'er you walk'? **c)** Who wrote, 'Where have all the flowers gone'?

GENERAL KNOWLEDGE 15

Starters

1. Karl Ritter is often referred to as the father of one of the modern academic studies. Which one?
2. Which famous school was endowed, together with a hospital and chapel, in 1611 by Thomas Sutton, on a site just west of Aldersgate in London?
3. Which modern sculptor has a bronze entitled 'Oval Form' in the Aberdeen Art Gallery?
4. Which explorer was the first to sail through the north-west passage, and fix the position of the north magnetic pole?
5. What is the better-known name of the Spanish hero Rodrigo Diaz de Vivar?
6. What is the name of one of the greatest elegiac poets of Rome, born in Assisium in the 1st century BC?
7. Which African republic was originally founded in 1822 as a community for freed slaves returning from America?
8. Which son of a famous novelist wrote *The Foxglove Saga* in 1960?
9. What was the family name of Lord Melbourne?
10. What part of a great queen's wardrobe equipment stands in Central Park, New York, and also on the Embankment in London?
11. What explosive powder was first manufactured at the Royal Gunpowder Factory, Waltham Abbey, in 1889?
12. When hydrogen has the number 1 what has the number 2?
13. In terms of liquids, fluidity is the reciprocal of what?
14. What is the derivation of the word 'navvy'?
15. What plant, in fable, because its forked root resembles the human form, was thought to shriek when plucked from the ground?

Answers on page 101

1. Who wrote the following?
   a) *Seven Types of Ambiguity* **b)** *The Seven Pillars of Wisdom* **c)** *Seven Against Thebes*

2. **a)** Which Shakespearean character said, 'O for a horse with wings'? **b)** Who eventually fell off a horse with wings? **c)** Who 'rode their horses up to bed'?

3. What are the original titles of these books?
   a) *Jeremie pêche à la ligne* **b)** *Hanes Meistres Tigi Dwt* **c)** *Petro Cuniculo*

4. **a)** What was the only way of getting a divorce in England before 1858? **b)** Which Archbishop helped to draft the *Reformatio Legum Ecclesiasticarum* in 1552, which would have introduced divorce into England? **c)** Which MP introduced a Private Member's Bill in 1937 increasing the number of grounds for divorce?

5. **a)** Where did the golden apples grow which were guarded by the dragon Ladon? **b)** Who killed the dragon Python, the guardian of Delphi? **c)** Who forced Hercules to fetch the guardian of the underworld, Cerberus?

6. **a)** With the plotting of whose death were the Casket Letters involved? **b)** To whom were the letters originally sent? **c)** Who used the letters as an excuse for a rebellion?

7. **a)** What group of seven were led by Pierre de Ronsard in the sixteenth century? **b)** From what did they take their name? **c)** From what did the Greeks take their name?

8. **a)** Which fortress was built in Northumberland in the 6th century by Ida? **b)** What is the name of the outcrop of rock on which it stands? **c)** The village is the birthplace of which famous 19th-century girl?

9. **a)** What familiar title did Tobias Smollett bestow on Dr Johnson? **b)** What title was held by the man who was called 'the Great Commoner'? **c)** Who was called 'the Great Nassau'?

10. **a)** What famous outlaw is buried in Balquhidder in Perthshire? **b)** What famous bandit was shot in the leg, his most vulnerable part, in 1880, and later captured and hanged? **c)** Which famous outlaw was called Locksley in Scott's *Ivanhoe*?

MYTHOLOGY AND ANCIENT HISTORY

Starters

1. Which architect successfully flew away from his irate patron, but whose unruly child failed to reach safety?
2. Who was the object of Oedipus' complex?
3. What 400-foot tower was built on an island off Alexandria and always had a wood fire burning at the top?
4. To whom was the temple, which stands on the promontory of Cape Sunion south-east of Athens, dedicated?
5. What bird, according to legend, did the Argonauts introduce into Europe?
6. Which city in Asia Minor is the site of the mausoleum built by Queen Artemisia in memory of her husband Mausolus?
7. Which famous legendary ship was commanded by Vanderdeken, who was condemned by his blasphemy to sail the seas until the Day of Judgement?
8. What fluid was supposed to flow in the veins of the Greek gods?
9. Which island was the traditional birthplace of Apollo?
10. Who was the first of the Flavian emperors of Rome?
11. What was the 'cloaca maxima'?
12. Who was the dwarf who guarded the ring of the Nibelungen?
13. Which composite creature had a lion's body, an eagle's head and sometimes had wings?
14. Who was killed when his horses broke their chariot traces, after being frightened by a monster from the sea?
15. What was the name given by the Ancient World to the planet Venus?

Bonus

Answers on page 102

1. **a)** Who lost a sandal and was therefore suspected by his half-uncle Pelias? **b)** Who was lent winged sandals to help him in the quest set by King Polydectes? **c)** Who found the sandal of his father, Aegeus, under a rock?

2. **a)** Where did the giants called Laestrygones live? **b)** What giant did Corineus defeat and throw into the sea, thus gaining Cornwall as a reward? **c)** Which giants lived on a small extension of land off North America and were discovered in the early 18th century?

3. **a)** What group did Aglaia, Euphrosyne and Thalia form? **b)** Who were Woglinde, Wellgunde and Flosshilde? **c)** Who were Tray, Blanch and Sweetheart?

4. **a)** What was the trade of Wayland? **b)** Who owned a sword called 'Nothung'? **c)** Who was the smith of the Greek gods?

5. **a)** What according to ancient writers made the apple of Sodom unpleasant to eat? **b)** What fruit is called 'the apple of love'? **c)** Who was awarded the 'apple of discord'?

6. What are the present-day names of these Roman towns?
a) Glevum **b)** Verulamium **c)** Deva

7. What are the modern names of these European cities?
a) Lutetia **b)** Lugdunum **c)** Lugdunum Batavorum

8. **a)** Which of the Fates, in Greek mythology, cut the thread of life? **b)** Which one held the distaff of life? **c)** Which one drew the threads of life and spun out the actions of life?

9. **a)** Which twins were born when Rhea Silvia, daughter of Numitor king of Alba Longa, was loved by the god Mars? **b)** Which twins were the brothers of Helen? **c)** What was the name of the famous twin brother of Iphicles?

10. **a)** Which queen of England, according to legend, fell in love with the son of Ban de Benoit? **b)** Which queen of Cornwall drank a love potion which bound her for ever to her husband's nephew? **c)** Who reputedly founded the city of Carthage?

GENERAL KNOWLEDGE 16

Starters

1. What is the 'Baconian Theory'?
2. Who bequeathed his second-best bed to his widow?
3. What is the more common name for the edible rounded bulb, *Allium cepa*?
4. What is the origin of the red and white spiral stripes on a barber's pole?
5. What do the initials ESP stand for?
6. Which colour is at the top of the rainbow?
7. What is the alternative name for mercury?
8. What name was given during World War II to the method of dispersing fog?
9. What is the popular name for nitrous oxide?
10. Who said in 1936, 'Guns will make us powerful, butter will only make us fat'?
11. Which Kent prison was taken over in 1912 'for the special location and treatment on reformatory lines of young prisoners'?
12. What is the function of the 'Devil's Advocate'?
13. Which mountain in the Lake District is formed by the two peaks of Pike O'Stickle and Harrison Stickle?
14. What is the common name for hemicrania?
15. Who had statues of Garibaldi, the infant Samson and Queen Victoria standing between flowers at his front door?

 Answers on page 103

1. **a)** Which birds breed in the Arctic and then travel over 11,000 miles to the Antarctic? **b)** What is the common name of the butterflies which migrate from North Africa to central and northern Europe? **c)** One species of animal breeds only in the Pribilof Islands and then migrates 3,000 miles to California—which animal is it?

2. **a)** Which ancient town on the north coast of Turkey was famed for its red earth? **b)** Which philosopher was born there in 412 BC? **c)** Which famous king was born there?

3. **a)** Who built the city of Antinoopolis in Egypt? **b)** Who built Bucephela in India? **c)** Where did Prince Llewellyn of Wales bury his favourite hound?

4. **a)** At which Congress was the perpetual neutrality of Switzerland agreed upon? **b)** Which other country was recognised as a perpetual neutral state in 1839? **c)** Which country refused to ratify the Treaty of Versailles?

5. **a)** What caused the death of Rupert Brooke on Skiros? **b)** What caused the death of Lord Byron on Missolonghi? **c)** Which poet died in Casa Guidi in Florence in 1861 having caught a severe chill?

6. In what months were these battles fought?
   a) The Charge of the Light Brigade **b)** Waterloo **c)** Culloden

7. **a)** Beside which house did the Colosseum in Rome stand? **b)** Who owned a house called Robin Hill? **c)** In the grounds of which house stands the old Temple Bar?

8. **a)** Which charioteer defends one end of Westminster Bridge? **b)** Which charioteer, created by Lewis Wallace, won a race in the time of Christ? **c)** Who drove the chariot of the sun across the sky for part of one day?

9. What was the object of each of these plots?
   a) Cato Street Conspiracy **b)** Francis Throckmorton Conspiracy of 1584 **c)** The Rye House Plot

10. **a)** Who used the name Kindergarten for his school in Germany in 1837? **b)** Who developed the idea with her 'Casa degli Bambini'? **c)** Where was Milner's Kindergarten?

GENERAL KNOWLEDGE 17

Starters

1. What is the name given to the temperature at which the vapour pressure of a liquid equals the pressure of the atmosphere above it?

2. Of what kind of measurement is a 'slug' a unit?

3. A sphinx usually has a woman's head and a lion's body. What sort of head does a criosphinx possess?

4. What land, in the legend of King Arthur, was said to have sunk '40 fathoms under the water'?

5. What word means: a type of lizard, a type of warship, a senior schoolchild and a detector of radio activity?

6. Who was the first woman MP to sit in the House of Commons?

7. What is nanism?

8. In which year was the act passed that forbade the wearing of the kilt in Scotland?

9. What is the name for a group of snipe?

10. Who first used the phrase 'Art for Art's sake'?

11. Which king of France was known as Louis the Fat?

12. Who wrote *The First Blast of the Trumpet against the Monstrous Regiment of Women*?

13. From which river in Asia Minor do we get the verb which means to wind at random?

14. What do the initials DOM on a Benedictine bottle stand for?

15. In which year was the first television signal sent across the Atlantic from London?

Bonus *Answers on page 104*

1. **a)** Who led the Jacobites when they took control of Perth after raising the standard at Glenfinnan in 1745? **b)** Who was the leader of the English at the raid of Prestonpans? **c)** At which English town did Charles Stuart order the retreat of the Scots?

2. **a)** Who succeeded Winston Churchill as First Lord of the Admiralty in 1915? **b)** Who succeeded Balfour as leader of the Conservatives in 1911? **c)** In whose administration in 1925 was Balfour Lord President?

3. What were you if you were originally
a) Not a barbarian **b)** Not a goy **c)** A Vandal

4. **a)** In which of the towns destroyed by Vesuvius in AD 79 did the Elder Pliny die? **b)** Which island volcano lies off Sicily? **c)** In which country is the 'Valley of Ten Thousand Smokes'?

5. **a)** Which baroque architect created the baldachin in St Peter's, Rome? **b)** Which saint did he portray 'in ecstasy'? **c)** What did he design for the Piazza Navona in Rome?

6. **a)** Of what type are the columns of the Parthenon? **b)** In which style was the Nike temple designed? **c)** Where is the missing caryatid from the caryatid porch of the Erechtheum?

7. **a)** What did Maundy Gregory sell, which caused a scandal? **b)** What did Van Meegeren sell in World War II? **c)** In support of which engineering project of the 1890s did a proposed lottery loan cause a scandal and the downfall of a government?

8. What is the more usual name for the following?
a) Red corundum **b)** Blue beryl **c)** Green beryl

9. **a)** Which House of Correction stood by the Fleet? **b)** Which prison formed the gatehouse of the Westgate of the City of London? **c)** Which prison stood in Southwark by the London house of the Bishop of Winchester?

10. **a)** Which Phoenician seaport was famous for silks? **b)** In which modern country is it situated? **c)** Which Roman historian described Cleopatra attending a banquet in the thin-spun clinging silk garments of this town?

RELIGIONS

Starters

1. By what sea does the disobedient wife of one of the better inhabitants of one of the local Plain towns stand to this day?
2. What is the name given to the first Gentiles to recognise the greatness of Christ?
3. Cain was a tiller of the ground. What was Abel?
4. How often is a new production of the Passion Play at Oberammergau staged?
5. Which biblical king suffered from a disease which in general terms is now known as lycanthropy?
6. Which saint's remains were stolen from Alexandria and smuggled into Venice described as pork?
7. With what event does the Pentateuch end?
8. Whom did Moses marry?
9. Whose Egyptian concubine produced Ishmael?
10. In which land, according to Genesis, was the Tower of Babel?
11. What word was used by the gnostics as a magical formula to ward off diseases and misfortune?
12. Which sect of the Shi'ite Moslems was founded in the 11th century by the Old Man of the Mountains?
13. Which German theologian was executed at Flossenburg in Bavaria in 1945?
14. What is the only possible outcome of a Conclave?
15. Who established the first Carthusian monastery in England?

Answers on page 105

1. **a)** Who was the famous son of St Helena? **b)** Which saint's real name was Marie Bernarde Soubirous? **c)** Who was the father of St Elizabeth of Hungary?

2. In which months are the following Christian festivals? **a)** Lammas **b)** Martinmas **c)** Michaelmas

3. **a)** 'Tell it not in Gath.' What? **b)** 'Would God I had died for thee O Absalom, my son, my son.' Who said this? **c)** I am escaped with the skin of my teeth.' Who?

4. **a)** Who was responsible for making the first 'Golden Calf'? **b)** Which Israelite king made two golden calves? **c)** What was the intention of the 'Golden Bull' of 1356?

5. **a)** What book follows 'Numbers' in the Authorised Version of the Bible? **b)** Which is the first book named after a man? **c)** Which is the first book to have a woman's name for a title?

6. Which town was the birthplace of each of these people? **a)** Abraham **b)** Goliath **c)** David

7. What rewards were promised to these people in the Beatitudes?
   a) The Poor in Spirit **b)** The Pure in Heart **c)** The Peacemakers

8. With which people in the Bible are these animals associated?
   a) Ant **b)** Ass **c)** Camel

9. **a)** To how many churches did John address his letter mentioned in *The Book of Revelation*? **b)** Name any two of them.

10. **a)** Of what religion was the Emperor of Japan traditionally the High Priest? **b)** Who is the hereditary spiritual leader of the Ismaili sect? **c)** What is the title of the person who presides over Presbyterian assemblies?

GENERAL KNOWLEDGE 18

Starters

1. What did Becky Sharp throw at Miss Pinkerton's Academy when she drove away on her last day?
2. Who was the first woman cabinet minister?
3. Who was the hero of a book of extravagant adventures written by R E Raspe in 1785?
4. Who was the architect of the Houses of Parliament which were rebuilt after the fire of 1834?
5. What was the basis of the feudal tax called cornage?
6. Which of the sons of Chronus helped Laomedon by building the walls of Troy?
7. When did the Black Death first appear in England?
8. In France it is called *tachisme*. What is it known as in the United States?
9. Where was the home of George Washington?
10. What did the German word 'Panzer' mean originally?
11. Who gave the name 'photon' to the quantum of radiant energy in 1905?
12. What is the name of the process in which iron is dipped into molten zinc to combat erosion?
13. What 20th-century British Foreign Secretary had only one hand?
14. What second law is examined by the 'Carnot' cycle?
15. What was the stage name of Jeanne Marie Bourgeois, the French comedienne who died in 1956?

 Answers on page 106

1. **a)** Who gave advice on *How to Make Friends and Influence People*? **b)** Who wrote *The Gentle Art of Making Enemies* in the 19th century? **c)** Who founded the Society of Friends in the 17th century?

2. **a)** In which country was the city of Sybaris? **b)** Which village in Nottinghamshire had a reputation for the paradoxical 'wisdom' of its inhabitants? **c)** Which modern city has also been given this name because of its wisecracking habits?

3. **a)** Who instigated the St Valentine's Day massacre in 1929? **b)** Which massacre broke out on 24 August 1572? **c)** A meeting on 16 August 1819 resulted in the killing or wounding of 600 people. Where?

4. Which three men did Louis XIV employ to create Versailles?

5. **a)** Which dog lives eternally underground? **b)** Whose dogs live eternally overhead? **c)** Which dog was immortalised in celluloid in 1943?

6. What is or was celebrated on these festivals?
   a) Yom Kippur **b)** Candlemas **c)** Saturnalia

7. **a)** Which Jewish philosopher was 'excommunicated' by the synagogue in 1656? **b)** Of which other philosopher's work did he make a geometrical version in 1663? **c)** Who were crypto Jews?

8. **a)** What are the largest living land mammals belonging to the order Proboscidea? **b)** What does proboscidiferous mean? **c)** Which Monotremata have elongated noses which they use in feeding?

9. Which three artists painted Mrs Siddons as Perdita?

10. **a)** Who married Mrs Porter in 1735? **b)** Which famous pupil did he have at his school at Edial? **c)** What twopenny sheet did he publish twice a week for two years, starting in 1750?

SCIENCE

Starters

1. What name is applied in the US to hydrous zinc silicate and in Britain to zinc carbonate?
2. Where would one see mollies, gouramies, guppies and sword tails?
3. What is the generic name given to the type of fossil ape whose bones were found in Kenya in 1931?
4. What metal does sphalarite chiefly produce?
5. One of the earliest sources of iron used by man was in origin extraterrestrial. What was it?
6. Some of the finest jargons are green, others brown, yellow or colourless. What are jargons in this context?
7. What did Thomas Boulsover produce by fixing a coating of silver over copper articles?
8. If ordinary oxygen in scientific terminology is O- what is called O_3?
9. Who prepared the first scientific list of elements in 1789?
10. *Hedera helix* is an evergreen woody climber. What is it?
11. What happens to fragments of obsidian when they are heated until they fuse?
12. What name is commonly given to the ulnar nerve where it lies on part of the humerus and is therefore exposed to contact?
13. What is the common name of the flower *Digitalis purpurea*?
14. What is the only temperature at which Centigrade and Fahrenheit thermometers both give the same reading?
15. Who discovered that the wavelengths of X-rays and gamma rays were reduced in frequency or increased in length when scattered by electrons?

 Answers on page 107

1. **a)** What is the branch of mechanics concerned with the phenomena of motion without reference to mass or force? **b)** What name is given to the energy which a body possesses by virtue of its motion? **c)** What branch of mechanics deals with the mathematical and physical study of the behaviour of bodies under the action of forces which produce changes in motion in them?

2. **a)** Where are the islets of Langerhans? **b)** Where are the Billroth cords? **c)** Where can Kupffer cells be found?

3. What are the four separate tastes which the taste buds can identify?

4. **a)** What is the vaccine BCG used to prevent? **b)** What do the initials stand for?

5. What three substances make up the alloy invar?

6. **a)** What is the usual name for a solution of hydrocyanic acid? **b)** Who discovered it in 1782? **c)** From what substance was it discovered?

7. **a)** Which Russian chemist in 1869 made the first periodic table of elements? **b)** Which German had independently reached a similar conclusion? **c)** Who devised the new table in 1895?

8. **a)** What is the clear form of quartz called? **b)** Which variety of quartz is green with red spots? **c)** Which variety of quartz is used for making cameos?

9. Which metals are obtained from the following ores?
   a) Bauxite **b)** Hematite **c)** Galena

10. Where are the following bones?
    a) Axis **b)** Sternum **c)** Tibia

GENERAL KNOWLEDGE 19

Starters

1. Which English poet's first book of verse was called *The Loom of Years*?
2. What is the modern name for Tyburn Road in London?
3. Who wrote the play *Chatterton* for Marie Duval?
4. What was the occupation of Ruy Blas, in one of Victor Hugo's plays?
5. In which country is the earth's north magnetic pole?
6. Where is the Cape Verde Basin?
7. What is missing from this list? Ruthenium, rhodium, palladium, osmium, iridium
8. Who wrote an essay on 'Murder considered as one of the Fine Arts'?
9. If a Rolls-Royce has a red rather than a black radiator badge, what does it mean?
10. What is the familiar name for the white solid which is natural hydrated magnesium silicate?
11. Which art gallery in London was first opened to the public in July 1962?
12. Who was the Union general in the American Civil War who stated, 'War is hell'?
13. Who was the first man recorded as having died on Mount Hor?
14. Who was the founder of Girton College, Cambridge?
15. Which waterway derives its name from the city where Sulla and Mithridates VI signed a treaty in 84 BC?

 Answers on page 108

1. **a)** Which saint gave half his cloak to a beggar at Amiens? **b)** Which saint took off his clothes and gave them to his father? **c)** Who won by lot an unseamed coat?

2. Name three of the five major states of 15th-century Italy.

3. **a)** What nation was accused of crossing the McMahon Line in August 1959? **b)** Who was prime minister of India at the time? **c)** Who visited New Delhi to discuss the problem in April 1960?

4. **a)** Whose friend and adviser was Piers Gaveston? **b)** Which of Arthur's knights was killed in the battle against Mordred? **c)** Whose friend was Enkidu?

5. **a)** Who produced the first set of mathematical tables in his *Almagest* in the 2nd century AD? **b)** Who produced a five-place table of sines in 1543? **c)** Who produced a table of eight-place logarithms in 1614?

6. **a)** Name the islands in the Aegean which literally mean 'scattered'. **b)** Which is the largest of the Friendly Islands? **c)** Which country controls the Society Islands?

7. Which three titles make up, with *Phineas Finn*, Trollope's series of novels on parliamentary life?

8. **a)** To which family of animals does the American Jack Rabbit belong? **b)** What type of animal is a Bombay Duck? **c)** To which family does the duckbill platypus belong?

9. **a)** Which author, well known for his amazing memory, was in Intelligence work during World War I? **b)** Which author worked as a war correspondent for the *New York Herald Tribune* in World War II? **c)** Which doctor, whose first novel appeared in 1897, worked as a secret agent during World War I?

10. **a)** What is the better-known name of the western wall of the Temple of Solomon? **b)** What is the name of the wall that runs from the Forth to the Clyde, built in the 2nd century AD? **c)** Which famous New York road stretches from Broadway to the East River?

GENERAL KNOWLEDGE 20

Starters

1. Who was the Minister of Food who introduced bread rationing in Britain in 1946?
2. When did Hansard begin?
3. Of what was 'ormolu' made?
4. Who wrote the poem that Sir Edward Elgar used as the text for *The Dream of Gerontius*?
5. At which Uruguayan port was the first industrialised meat-packing plant established in 1861?
6. In which country is the Malabar coast?
7. Who received the last measure of wine, after bringing good news from Ghent to Aix?
8. What was Piccadilly Circus called when it was opened in 1819?
9. Which mineral is the chief commercial source of potassium compounds?
10. Who was the first president of the USA to live in the White House?
11. In which film was the 4th Movement of Mahler's Symphony No 5 used as background music?
12. Who was Zuleika Dobson?
13. What reason does Coleridge give for the Ancient Mariner killing the albatross?
14. What was the first of the twelve labours of Hercules?
15. What are a burgonet, a bascinet and a morion?

Answers on page 109

Bonus

1. **a)** Which country was described in Genesis as stretching from Gaza to Sidon? **b)** Which hero was crushed in Gaza in a Holy Temple? **c)** Who reduced Gaza to ruins in 332 BC?

2. **a)** Who was specially marked to prevent his being murdered? **b)** What was stolen from Adam while he slept? **c)** Who said, 'I have gotten a man'?

3. **a)** Which French queen was involved in the 'Affair of the Diamond Necklace'? **b)** Who owns a diamond which she calls 'The Ping Pong' diamond? **c)** Which company controls almost the entire world output of diamonds?

4. **a)** Which object did Van Gogh paint lying on the seat of the straw-bottomed chair? **b)** What creature did Chardin paint in his still life *The Skate*? **c)** What is Cupid holding in the Velasquez *Rokeby Venus*?

5. **a)** Who, according to Christopher Hill, was 'God's Englishman'? **b)** What does a 'God's Advocate' advocate? **c)** What was God's Sunday?

6. **a)** What is missing from the pig-like animal, the peccary? **b)** What is unique about the loss of antlers by the Père David deer? **c)** What have Cape hunting dogs got which makes them fundamentally different from all other dogs?

7. In which books do these convicts appear?
a) Kags **b)** 105 North Tower **c)** Abel Magwitch

8. **a)** Who collaborated to write *The Tender Husband* in 1705? **b)** What did one of them support in a pamphlet *The Crisis* in 1714? **c)** What was the cause of their estrangement shortly before the death of one of them?

9. Name any three countries, south of the Panama Canal, which have a coastline on the Pacific Ocean.

10. **a)** Who dreamt about fourteen members of the bovine family, some fatter than the others? **b)** Whose work on dreams was published in *The Interpretation of Dreams* in 1900? **c)** Where did Mr Lockwood dream he heard a sermon based on '70 times 7' and woke to find a ghost at his window?

SPORTS AND PASTIMES

Starters

1. Which five-a-side game was invented by James Naismith at the end of the 19th century?

2. What game is played on an area some 300 yards by 200 yards, in which the match lasts about an hour and ends are changed after each goal?

3. What is 4 miles 856 yards long, takes about 10 minutes to cover and contains 30 obstacles?

4. What is still killed with a sword called an *estoque?*

5. In which card game does Blücher count for more than Wellington, and Wellington for more than Napoleon?

6. When KB2 = KB7 what does QR5 equal?

7. Whose treatise on whist was first published in 1742?

8. What measure of length was a Stadium?

9. Who won all three Olympic long-distance running titles?

10. What game is won in one round by a score of 61, and in two rounds by a score of 121?

11. At which Olympic Games was judo first included?

12. When was a cricketer entitled to a new cap from his club?

13. What is the name of the British air race which has been held annually since 1922 (except during World War II)?

14. Which king, in a standard British pack of playing cards, has only one eye?

15. What is the origin of the word 'checkmate' in chess?

Bonus

Answers on page 110

1. **a)** In which sport was the four-hour barrier for 100 miles distance broken in 1956? **b)** Who held the record after Bannister for the sub-four-minute mile? **c)** Which height did Charles Dumas clear in the high jump in 1956?

2. In May 1947 a football team representing Great Britain played a match at Hampden Park to celebrate the return of the British Football Association to the International Federation.
   a) Who were the opponents? **b)** Who captained the Great Britain side? **c)** Who won the match?

3. **a)**Which sports use the following terms?
   a) Free position, draw, stand **b)** Coup de cabasse, dedans, hazard side **c)** Touchers, ditches, kitties

4. **a)** In which year was the first world speed record of over 1,000 mph set? **b)** Who was the pilot? **c)** What kind of aircraft did he fly?

5. In international motor racing what colours are the cars of the following countries?
   a) France **b)** Italy **c)** Germany

6. Where are the following Classic races held?
   a) The St Leger **b)** The Oaks **c)** The Two Thousand Guineas

7. On which ground do the following football teams play?
   a) Everton **b)** Sheffield Wednesday **c)** Liverpool

8. **a)** When were the first modern Olympic Games held? **b)** When was the British Olympic Association founded? **c)** What was the best performance in the Men's 100 metres in 1924?

9. **a)** What was the origin of lawn tennis in the latter part of the 18th century? **b)** What was the name given to the game invented by Major Wingfield in 1874? **c)** Which club drew up the first code of rules for lawn tennis in 1875?

10. **a)** When was the Marylebone Cricket Club formed? **b)** When was the present Lord's ground opened? **c)** Who invented the 'googly'?

GENERAL KNOWLEDGE 21

Starters

1. What poem was described as 'An Agony in Eight Fits'?
2. How many members should there be in a witches' coven?
3. By what name is the painter Domenicos Theotocopoulos better known?
4. What is the connection between the Duke of Burgundy, the Painted Lady and the Red Admiral?
5. Which English king was killed while besieging the castle of Châlons in France?
6. In Rudyard Kipling's book, *Kim*, what was Kim's surname?
7. What, according to Shelley, had a mask like Castlereagh?
8. Who composed *Curlew River*?
9. Which country, by the Treaty of Kiel in 1814, ceded Norway to Sweden?
10. Who was the 'merry wanderer of the night'?
11. Which of the twelve tribes of Israel did not receive an inheritance in the Promised Land?
12. When was the name of Windsor adopted by the Royal Family?
13. What is a Rechabite?
14. Who was the Divine Sarah?
15. What nationality was the first man to reach the North Pole?

 Answers on page 111

1. **a)** Whose autobiography, written in the 17th century, was entitled *Grace Abounding*? **b)** Whose autobiography was entitled *The Greatest*? **c)** Whose 14th-century biographical account of the life of Dante is the source of much of the information about the poet?

2. **a)** Which expedition did Lewis and Clark undertake in 1804—6? **b)** In exploring which country did Burke and Wills die? **c)** What great discovery did Speke and Burton disagree about in 1858?

3. **a)** Who was experimenting with a miners' 'safety lamp' design at the same time as Humphry Davy? **b)** Which company offered a prize of £500 for a railway engine? **c)** Who constructed a steam carriage in Cornwall in 1802?

4. **a)** Which planet has a sidereal revolution of 4,333 days? **b)** What became specially prominent on it in 1878? **c)** How many of its satellites make up the Galilean Satellites?

5. **a)** Who, in the Bible, journeyed to Joppa against orders and got caught in a storm? **b)** What land lay on the other side of the Sea of Galilee from Galilee? **c)** After the forty days and nights of rain of the Flood, how long did the waters prevail upon the earth?

6. To what dates do these quotations refer?
   a) 'God blew and they were scattered.' **b)** 'What shall we do with this bauble? Take it away.' **c)** 'The House of Commons, Sir, is inclined to Mercy.'

7. **a)** Which maidens, in the *Iliad*, guarded the gates of Olympus? **b)** Which maidens guarded the golden apples? **c)** Which three old women had long grey hair and only one eye and one tooth between them?

8. **a)** What did the Spartan King Leonidas hold for three days against overwhelming odds? **b)** What was the last name of the man who held the Sublician Bridge against the Etruscan army? **c)** Who took and sacked the city of Calcutta in 1756?

9. **a)** What is the name of the tributary of the Scheldt on which Brussels stands? **b)** Who is referred to by the people of Brussels as their oldest citizen? **c)** What is the name of the ship canal which connects Antwerp and Brussels?

THEATRE AND CINEMA

Starters

1. Which English playwright acted under the name of David Baron?

2 Which great showman styled himself 'The Prince of Humbugs'?

3. Which famous film director was at one time the tennis champion of North Italy and ended one of his films with a most unusual tennis match?

4. Which role has been played on the cinema screen by John Barrymore, Clive Brook, John Neville, Raymond Massey, Basil Rathbone, Peter Cushing and Robert Stephens?

5. Which famous team made films which included two Nights and one Day?

6. Which playwright contrived some entertainment for Mr Sloan?

7. Which playwright's interest in Dunne's theory of time was expressed in his first play *Dangerous Corner*?

8. What sign, according to the music-hall legend, did Vernon Watson see in a railway carriage and adopt as his stage name?

9. What play was Molière performing in 1673 when he fell mortally ill in the middle of the performance?

10. What film, shortly after the outbreak of World War II, had its première in Atlanta, Georgia?

11. By what other name was Baroness Cederstrom known?

12. Where did Holly Golightly dream of having breakfast?

13. Which actor made his début in London on 26 January 1814, as Shylock?

14. Who was the lover's go-between in *Troilus and Cressida*?

15. Who was the actress Mrs Eleanor Gwyn?

Bonus

Answers on page 112

1. **a)** Who wrote the screenplay of *The Misfits* in 1961 for his second wife? **b)** Which star died within a month of the completion of its filming? **c)** Who produced the film?

2. **a)** Who said: 'Friends, I owe more tears / To this dead man than you shall see me pay'? **b)** Who is the dead man? **c)** Where were the words said?

3. **a)** In which country was Al Jolson born? **b)** What was the name of the film which was the first important talking picture? **c)** Who played Jolson in *The Jolson Story*?

4. What sports are involved in these films?
   a) *Endless Summer* **b)** *This Sporting Life* **c)** *Downhill Racer*

5. **a)** Who were the two merry wives of Windsor? **b)** Whose son said, 'A sad tale's best for winter'? **c)** Romeo loved Juliet in Verona. In which of Shakespeare's plays did Claudio love Juliet in Vienna?

6. What were these Shakespearean characters' professions?
   a) Dogberry **b)** Christopher Sly **c)** Sir Hugh Evans

7. In the Savoy operas who
   a) Maintained that man is nature's sole mistake? **b)** Was familiar with the frogs? **c)** Was a dealer in magic and spells?

8. **a)** Near which city is Mozart's opera *Don Giovanni* set? **b)** Who wrote *Don Juan ou le Festin de Pierre* in 1665? **c)** In Which of Shaw's plays is 'Don Juan the quarry instead of the huntsman'?

9. In which plays do the following characters appear?
   a) Captain Jack Boyle **b)** Willy Loman **c)** Harry, Lord Monchensey

10. **a)** What nationality was Doctor Caius in *The Merry Wives of Windsor*? **b)** What is the profession of Sir Oliver Martext in *As You Like It*? **c)** What is Lavache in *All's Well that Ends Well*?

Answers

GENERAL KNOWLEDGE 1

Starters ***Answers to pages 8 and 9***

1. Salted (beef preserved by salting) **2.** Lancelot Brown (Capability) **3.** All were drowned at sea **4.** Gunter's **5.** Gargoyle (from *gargouille*) **6.** Blaise Pascal **7.** None **8.** Ismailia **9.** *Marie Celeste* **10.** Charles Dickens **11.** Aeroplane accidents (Midas flight recorder) **12.** Fillet steak **13.** Jean Baptiste Pierre Lamarck **14.** Bournville **15.** Lances

Bonus

1. **a)** Gurkhas **b)** Malaya **c)** South African tribes
2. **a)** Copenhagen **b)** Brussels **c)** Amsterdam
3. **a)** Seaweed **b)** A tree from southern and tropical Africa **c)** Rio de Janeiro
4. **a)** Balzac **b)** 'The Thinker' **c)** Rainer Maria Rilke
5. **a)** Anabaptists **b)** Society of Friends (Quakers) **c)** H R L (Dick) Sheppard
6. **a)** Bay **b)** Garlic **c)** Strawberry
7. **a)** Thursday **b)** Thursday **c)** Tuesday
8. **a)** The Knesset **b)** Count Bernadotte of Wisburg **c)** Chaim Weizmann
9. **a)** Polynesian **b)** Dutch **c)** French (from the Italian *Tarocco*)
10. **a)** Charlotte **b)** Etruria **c)** He was Darwin's grandfather

GENERAL KNOWLEDGE 2

Starters

Answers to pages 10 and 11

1. Jade **2.** Sir Walter Scott **3.** Weimar **4.** Tea **5.** Padua **6.** Robert Stephenson **7.** Neil Armstrong **8.** *The Magic Roundabout* **9.** Bramante **10.** Germanium **11.** Egypt **12.** Nansen passport **13.** Count Rasumovsky **14.** A Communist **15.** Lyonnesse

Bonus

1. **a)** Simon de Montfort **b)** Henry III **c)** Evesham (1265)

2. Greece, Turkey, Romania, Yugoslavia

3. **a)** Eastern Europe and Western Asia **b)** America (Central) **c)** Africa (Southern)

4. **a)** David Livingstone **b)** Albert Schweitzer **c)** Kwame Nkrumah

5. **a)** Its glance could kill **b)** Polydectes **c)** Arizona

6. **a)** Waterloo (1815) **b)** Hiroshima (1945) **c)** London (1665, Great Plague)

7. **a)** British Museum **b)** Victoria and Albert Museum **c)** Trinity College, Dublin

8. **a)** Botanists **b)** Bankers or merchants **c)** Lexicographers

9. **a)** Oil **b)** Banking **c)** Telegraphy

10. **a)** The birthright of Esau **b)** Alaska **c)** Peacock's tail

ART AND ARCHITECTURE

Starters

Answers to pages 12 and 13

1. Constantin Brancusi **2.** Mildenhall Treasure **3.** Paul Gauguin **4.** The Elgin Marbles **5.** Barcelona **6.** Le Corbusier **7.** Rembrandt (Van Rijn) **8.** John Piper **9.** In the Vatican Museum **10.** Sir Joshua Reynolds **11.** Frank Lloyd Wright **12.** Salvador Dali **13.** James McNeill Whistler **14.** Augustus Pugin **15.** Sir John Millais

Bonus

1. **a)** Francisco Goya **b)** Jean Géricault **c)** Vincent Van Gogh

2. **a)** Austria **b)** Titian (Tiziano Vecelli) **c)** Praxiteles

3. **a)** Donatello (Donato di Niccoló) **b)** Joan of Arc **c)** Richard I

4. **a)** Jean Baptiste Corot **b)** Meindert Hobbema **c)** Jean François Millet

5. **a)** Sir Basil Spence **b)** John Nash **c)** Inigo Jones

6. **a)** Francisco Goya y Lucientes **b)** Sir Stanley Spencer **c)** Honoré Daumier

7. **a)** Sir John Millais **b)** William Holman Hunt **c)** Gabriel Charles Dante Rossetti

8. **a)** Francis I of France **b)** Ludovico Sforza of Milan **c)** Czar Alexander III

9. **a)** Nicolas **b)** Aristide **c)** Amedeo

10. **a)** William Shakespeare **b)** The wife of Francesco di Bartolomeo del Giocondo **c)** Mrs Sarah Siddons

GENERAL KNOWLEDGE 3

Starters

Answers to pages 14 and 15

1. Battleships **2.** William E Gladstone **3.** Thirty minutes **4.** General Mohammed Neguib **5.** Mississippi **6.** £⅔ (66p) **7.** Banishment from Attica for ten years **8.** Cows **9.** London **10.** Earldom of Sussex **11.** Theory of evolution as stated in Darwin's *The Origin of Species* **12.** Dollar (from thaler) town **13.** Zeppelin airships **14.** Pogrom (devastation or riot) **15.** Ischia

Bonus

1. **a)** Red **b)** White **c)** Blue

2. **a)** Anton Bruckner (the other two were unfinished symphonies) **b)** *The Father* by August Strindberg (others by Anton Chekhov) **c)** *ABC of Naval Trainee* is World War II (others World War I)

3. **a)** 12 lbs (English 112 lbs; US 100 lbs) **b)** 240 lbs (English 2240 lbs; US 2000 lbs) **c)** A long or gross ton

4. **a)** Cairo **b)** Saladin **c)** Cairo

5. **a)** Mary Hogarth **b)** Elizabeth Patterson **c)** Mary of Modena

6. **a)** Trilby **b)** Princess Elizabeth (later Elizabeth I) **c)** Helen Keller

7. **a)** Sir Thomas Sopwith **b)** Rose Macaulay's in *The Towers of Trebizond* **c)** The Djinn of all the Deserts (*Just So Stories*)

8. **a)** Davy Crockett **b)** The Creek War **c)** Santa Anna

9. **a)** *The Charge of the Light Brigade*, Alfred Lord Tennyson **b)** Goliath **c)** The fathom

ASTRONOMY

Starters

Answers to pages 16 and 17

1. A star **2.** Aries (the others are water signs) **3.** Ferdinand Magellan (Magellanic clouds) **4.** Johann Kepler (1571—1630) **5.** Galileo Galilei **6.** 1957, 4 October (Sputnik I) **7.** David Fabricíus **8.** The nebulous envelope around the nucleus **9.** In the outer atmosphere **10.** Uranus **11.** The gap between the two outer rings of Saturn **12.** Around Saturn (it is one of its moons) **13.** The point of a planet's orbit furthest from the sun **14.** Pendulum (later) Gyroscope **15.** 8 minutes 14.6 seconds

Bonus

1. **a)** Aries **b)** Orion **c)** Ursa Major (Great Bear)

2. **a)** Apollo 12 **b)** Apollo 14 (Al Shepherd) **c)** 1967 (January)

3. **a)** Mercury and Venus **b)** Mars **c)** Jupiter

4. Gemini (heavenly twins); Virgo (virgin); Aquarius (water carrier)

5. **a)** Saros **b)** Thales (640 BC) **c)** Pythagoras

6. **a)** E W Brown's **b)** Gustav Robert Kirchhoff's **c)** The brightness of stars

7. **a)** 1986 **b)** Kohoutek **c)** Beggars *(Julius Caesar,* Act II)

8. **a)** Sir Arthur Stanley Eddington **b)** Edward Emerson Barnard **c)** Sir Frederick William Herschel

9. **a)** Uranus **b)** Neptune **c)** Pluto

10. **a)** Six **b)** Hipparchus **c)** Colour index

GENERAL KNOWLEDGE 4

Starters

Answers to pages 18 and 19

1. 1666 *(MDCLXVI)* **2.** The seven sleepers of Ephesus **3.** Punch **4.** Finger-prints **5.** Tailoring (measurements for a jacket are always given in this sequence) **6.** Ferret **7.** Big Ben **8.** Alfred C Kinsey **9.** Romany **10.** A sea bird (a tern) **11.** Snoek **12.** A spider's web **13.** 1919 **14.** Ford Motor Company **15.** Self-rule

Bonus

1. **a)** Madagascar **b)** Central Africa **c)** Southern Asia
2. **a)** The Medici **b)** Red fleur de lis **c)** St John the Baptist
3. **a)** The English-speaking Presbyterians during the Civil War **b)** Thomas de Quincey **c)** Jean-Jacques Rousseau
4. **a)** Gethsemane **b)** Letchworth **c)** Hieronymus Bosch
5. **a)** Palaeontology **b)** Serology **c)** Ballistics
6. **a)** Grouse **b)** Plover **c)** Bunting
7. **a)** Alpaca or llama **b)** One **c)** Bactrian camel
8. **a)** Volcanoes **b)** Republic of Mali **c)** Uzbekistan
9. **a)** Astronomy **b)** Painting of miniatures **c)** Surgery
10. **a)** Anthony Powell (in the 12 volumes of *A Dance to the Music of Time)* **b)** Lawrence Durrell (in the *Alexandria Quartet*) **c)** Simon Raven (in the 10 volumes of *Alms for Oblivion)*

GENERAL KNOWLEDGE 5

Starters ***Answers to pages 20 and 21***

1. Melbourne **2.** Countess of Warwick **3.** The Pre-Raphaelites **4.** *The Blue Boy* **5.** Five **6.** Lewis Carroll (in *Through the Looking-glass*) **7.** Kubla Khan **8.** Absinthe **9.** They are for flying **10.** Thor **11.** Robert Edwin Peary **12.** Graf Maximilian Von Spee **13.** Notre-Dame de Paris **14.** Viscount **15.** Chess

Bonus

1. **a)** Poliomyelitis **b)** Epilepsy **c)** A stammer

2. **a)** Pomona (or Mainland) **b)** Tenerife **c)** Luzon

3. **a)** Earl of Aberdeen **b)** H H Asquith **c)** Stanley Baldwin

4. **a)** Delaware **b)** Wyoming **c)** North Dakota

5. **a)** Nephew **b)** Olivia **c)** Little Emily

6. **a)** Harry S Truman **b)** Lord Salisbury **c)** René Coty

7. **a)** Self-incrimination (against) **b)** Slavery (abolished) **c)** Prohibition (instituted)

8. **a)** A ring (*The Owl and the Pussycat*) **b)** Dukes (*The Gondoliers*) **c)** Hot cross buns

9. **a)** Butterfly **b)** Bird **c)** Reptile

10. **a)** St Thomas's **b)** Guy's **c)** St Mary's

GEOGRAPHY

Starters

Answers to pages 22 and 23

1. River Rhône **2.** Portugal and western Spain (Roman names) **3.** River Shannon **4.** River **5.** Caldy (Ynys Byr) **6.** Magenta **7.** Muckle Flugga lighthouse **8.** Furness **9.** Chesil Bank **10.** The Canary Islands **11.** Mascarene Islands **12.** Navigating by following railway lines **13.** Turin **14.** Lake Baikal, Siberia **15.** La Paz (Bolivia)

Bonus

1. **a)** Solomon Islands **b)** Fiji Islands **c)** Society Islands
2. **a)** Lake Erie; Lake Ontario **b)** River Niagara
3. Bronx; Brooklyn; Queens; Richmond
4. Neva; Vistula; Oder
5. **a)** All are Norfolk Broads **b)** All are caves **c)** All are forests
6. **a)** The Black Sea **b)** Bosphorus and the Persian Gulf **c)** Gwynedd
7. **a)** Tigris **b)** Khartoum **c)** Salisbury
8. **a)** Texas **b)** Alaska **c)** Pennsylvania
9. **a)** Mersey **b)** Milan **c)** Road to the Isles
10. Turkey; Syria; USSR

GENERAL KNOWLEDGE 6

Starters ***Answers to pages 24 and 25***

1. Paul Julius Reuter **2.** Rhinoceros **3.** Calendar of the French Revolution **4.** Camels (Imperial Camel Corps Brigade) **5.** Rhubarb **6.** Tin Pan Alley **7.** Oceana **8.** Charlotte Corday (she stabbed Jean Paul Marat) **9.** Comic strips—cartoon strips **10.** Peanut (groundnut) **11.** Enrique Granados (on a channel steamer off Sussex) **12.** Pearl **13.** Boers of South Africa **14.** Pyramid **15.** Nectarine

Bonus

1. **a)** Wilkie Collins (*The Moonstone*) **b)** G K Chesterton (the *Father Brown* stories) **c)** Charles Dickens (*Bleak House*)

2. **a)** Portugal **b)** Italy **c)** Germany

3. **a)** Arabia **b)** Bay of Bengal **c)** Strait of Malacca

4. **a)** South Stack **b)** Skerryvore **c)** Bell Rock or Inchcape Rock

5. **a)** Edward Jenner **b)** W G Grace **c)** Edward Wilson

6. **a)** Jane **b)** Crippen **c)** Pincushion

7. **a)** Thomas Jefferson **b)** Abraham Lincoln **c)** Andrew Jackson

8. **a)** South Africa **b)** India **c)** Arabian countries (Near East and North Africa)

9. **a)** A person who eats dirts **b)** A mammal which walks on the soles of its feet with the heel touching the ground (i.e. bears, man) **c)** A person who studies ferns

10. **a)** Comintern (Communist International) **b)** International Working Men's Association **c)** Cominform (Communist Information Bureau)

HISTORY 1

Starters

Answers to pages 26 and 27

1. Henry II (in penance for Thomas à Becket's death) **2.** Jean Baptiste Colbert **3.** 1189 **4.** Declaration of Independence **5.** Aachen (Aix-la-Chapelle) **6.** Public conveniences **7.** Thugs **8.** John Brown **9.** Richard II **10.** Bayeux in France (tapestry) **11.** Stephen Langton **12.** Archimedes **13.** Mohammed's **14.** Judge Jeffreys' **15.** Corsica (Napoleon Bonaparte)

Bonus

1. Jedburgh; Melrose; Dryburgh; Kelso

2. **a)** Bartolomeo Dias de Novae **b)** John II **c)** Vasco da Gama

3. **a)** Frederick Louis **b)** John of Gaunt **c)** Ernest Augustus

4. **a)** Kubla Khan **b)** Tamberlaine (Timur) **c)** Montezuma

5. **a)** Boston **b)** Colonel George Washington **c)** Major-General William Howe

6. **a)** Beau Brummel **b)** Falstaff **c)** Sarah Churchill, Duchess of Marlborough

7. **a)** Spain **b)** Holland **c)** Westphalia

8. **a)** Sprig of broom **b)** The price tag **c)** Augustus

9. **a)** Pope Leo X **b)** Medici **c)** Martin Luther

10. **a)** Priam **b)** Manuel II **c)** George VI

GENERAL KNOWLEDGE 7

Starters ***Answers to pages 28 and 29***

1. Nutmeg **2.** Magnesium **3.** Commander-in-chief of the Japanese army **4.** Pemmican **5.** Lameness **6.** Walloons **7.** Fianna Fail **8.** John Adams **9.** Pierre and Marie Curie **10.** Ming **11.** Right-angled triangle **12.** Thomas R Malthus **13.** Six **14.** Yellow fever **15.** Inside a bone

Bonus

1. **a)** Rue **b)** Three **c)** Because the initials DG (By the Grace of God, *Dei Gratia*) and FD (Defender of the Faith, *Fidei Defensor*) were omitted.

2. **a)** Chile **b)** Zaire **c)** USA

3. **a)** Matthew Arnold (*A Summer Night*) **b)** William Wordsworth (*Ode on Intimations of Immortality*) **c)** Richard Lovelace (*To Althea from Prison*)

4. **a)** Edward VI **b)** Henry VI **c)** Henry III

5. **a)** School teacher (Muriel Spark) **b)** A hangman (Charles Dickens) **c)** Butler (Sir Walter Scott)

6. **a)** Fujiyama **b)** Vesuvius **c)** Tristan da Cunha

7. **a)** Desdemona (in *Othello*) **b)** Mrs Tiggy-Winkle (in *The Tale of Mrs Tiggy-Winkle*) **c)** The Walrus (in *Through the Looking-Glass* by Lewis Carroll)

8. **a)** The Palace of Westminster **b)** Thomas Wolsey **c)** The Long Parliament (1641)

GENERAL KNOWLEDGE 8

Starters

Answers to pages 30 and 31

1. Neapolitan secret society of the 19th century **2.** The ostrich **3.** All are varieties of gooseberry **4.** Hypermetropia **5.** Beecham's Pills **6.** Loss of sense of smell **7.** Lord Mayor of London **8.** Alexander Popov **9.** All are blood groups of man **10.** Gladiolus **11.** Anthony Trollope **12.** Frog-like **13.** For the murder of Thomas à Becket **14.** Worms **15.** Nothing. These were the days lost by the change to the Gregorian calendar

Bonus

1. **a)** Hercules **b)** Patroclus **c)** Jason

2. **a)** Federal *v* Confederate army (Richmond 1862) **b)** Prussia *v* Austria, Saxony, Hanover (1866) **c)** Prussia and England *v* Austria, France, Russia, Sweden, Saxony (1756-63)

3. **a)** Henry Brougham **b)** William IV **c)** Lord John Russell

4. **a)** In the area between the Tigris and Euphrates **b)** Nineveh **c)** Jonah

5. **a)** Brazil **b)** Venezuela **c)** Arctic Circle

6. **a)** Rabbit **b)** Wren **c)** Robin

7. **a)** Chequers, to serve as a country residence of the prime minister of the day **b)** Osborne, Isle of Wight **c)** Office of the Government Whips

8. Francis II (1559—60); Charles IX (1560—74); Henry III (1574—89)

9. **a)** Cecil Rhodes **b)** Kimberley (Earl of) **c)** De Beers Mining Company

10. **a)** A granny knot **b)** A clock **c)** A harvestman (Daddy Longlegs)

HISTORY 2

Starters **Answers to pages 32 and 33**

1. All were anti-popes **2.** Cardinal Wolsey's **3.** On the HMV gramophone label **4.** St Basil **5.** Arthur Wellesley (Duke of Wellington) **6.** Prestonpans **7.** Suttee **8.** On USS *Missouri* in Tokyo Bay **9.** Bullion depository at Fort Knox **10.** Franco-Prussian War of 1870—71 **11.** Frederick the Great of Prussia **12.** The Siegfried Line **13.** Captain Robert Falcon Scott's **14.** Charles I (Charles V of the Holy Roman Empire) **15.** Crossbow

Bonus

1. Denzil Holles; Sir Arthur Heselrige; William Strode

2. **a)** Queen Victoria **b)** George V **c)** Edward VII

3. **a)** Lord George Gordon **b)** Chartist **c)** Twelve persons or more

4. **a)** Siena **b)** Napoleon Bonaparte's **c)** Paul V

5. **a)** Copyright of artist's own designs **b)** Gregor Mendel's **c)** Licensing Act

6. **a)** Richard III **b)** James IV of Scotland **c)** Harold

7. Octavius Caesar; Mark Antony; Marcus Aemilius Lepidus

8. **a)** World War II (1941) **b)** American War of Independence (1776) **c)** Punic War II (202 BC)

9. **a)** 1928 **b)** 1903 **c)** 1963

10. **a)** Cato **b)** Daniel Defoe **c)** Kim Philby

GENERAL KNOWLEDGE 9

Starters

Answers to pages 34 and 35

1. For being a spiritualist medium **2.** Divers **3.** Chaos **4.** Molly Malone (cockles and mussels) **5.** George II **6.** A boat **7.** Palm of the hand (palmistry) **8.** Mumps **9.** Distillation (a type of still) **10.** Halogens **11.** Captain Joshua Slocum (completed 1898) **12.** Dewey decimal classification **13.** Sir Humphry Davy **14.** Cousin **15.** John Ray (Wray)

Bonus

1. **a)** Jean de Brunhof **b)** Igor Stravinsky (*The Rake's Progress*) **c)** Sir Richard Burton in his translation of *A Thousand and One Nights*

2. **a)** Medea **b)** Shangri La **c)** Princess Aurora

3. **a)** Gulf of Finland **b)** Caspian Sea **c)** The Sea of Japan

4. **a)** Winchester **b)** Gloucester **c)** East Anglia

5. **a)** West Berlin **b)** Calcutta **c)** Copenhagen

6. **a)** Walrus (from Lapp *morsa*) **b)** Telegraphic code (from S F B Morse) **c)** Clasp of a cape (from *morsus*: Latin 'catch' or 'bite)

7. **a)** Somerset **b)** Durham **c)** Cornwall

8. **a)** Solomon's Temple **b)** Great Temple of Amun **c)** The Temple of the Tooth

9. **a)** A youngest and favourite son **b)** A confirmed bachelor who marries **c)** A bearer of ill-luck

10. **a)** The Milky Way **b)** *The Way of All Flesh* by Samuel Butler **c)** *The Way of the World* by William Congreve

LITERATURE 1

Starters

Answers to pages 36 and 37

1. William Wordsworth **2.** Hercule Poirot **3.** Tom Snout, tinker (*A Midsummer Night's Dream*) **4.** Arthur Hallam's (*In Memoriam* by Alfred Lord Tennyson) **5.** Henry W Longfellow **6.** Hablot Knight Browne (Phiz) **7.** Catalectic **8.** George Eliot **9.** Humpty Dumpty **10.** Salem **11.** None **12.** *A Thousand and One Nights (Arabian Nights)* **13.** Ninotchka **14.** Simone de Beauvoir's **15.** Tabitha Twitchit

Bonus

1. **a)** Mr Wardle (in *The Pickwick Papers*, Charles Dickens) **b)** George and Vulture **c)** Eatanswill

2. **a)** Jean Anouilh **b)** Hugo von Hofmannstahl **c)** Jean Cocteau

3. **a)** 'cos they hadn't got a rabbit, not anywhere there' ('Market Square', A A Milne) **b)** 'And dances with the daffodils' ('The Daffodils', William Wordsworth) **c)** 'In hearts at peace, under an English heaven' ('The Soldier', Rupert Brooke)

4. **a)** Barnabas (in *The Jew of Malta,* Christopher Marlowe) **b)** Charles Pooter (George and Weedon Grossmith) **c)** Argan (in *Le Malade Imaginaire,* Molière)

5. **a)** Nancy (*Oliver Twist*) **b)** Dulcinea del Toboso **c)** *The Cloister and the Hearth* (Charles Reade)

6. **a)** Uriah Heep *(David Copperfield)* **b)** Stella Gibbons *(Cold Comfort Farm)* **c)** James James Morrison Morrison Weatherby George Dupree (A A Milne)

7. **a)** Elaine (in the poem by Alfred Lord Tennyson) **b)** John Milton (in *Brief Lives*, John Aubrey) **c)** Cassiopeia

8. **a)** Immortality **b)** Eros **c)** Titania

9. **a)** John Gilpin **b)** 'The Ancient Mariner' (Samuel T Coleridge) **c)** Petruchio (*The Taming of the Shrew*)

GENERAL KNOWLEDGE 10

Starters

Answers to pages 38 and 39

1. Preventing rust forming on cast iron **2.** Joachim Murat **3.** From the Roman word for 'pebble' **4.** Tremadoc, North Wales, 1888 **5.** A fish **6.** Viscount Grey of Fallodon **7.** 1873 **8.** Suit of armour **9.** All are stations on the Métro **10.** Sedgemoor (1685) **11.** Ireland **12.** Sir Stafford Cripps **13.** Peccary **14.** Czar Nicholas I of Russia **15.** Sequoia

Bonus

1. **a)** Nevil Shute **b)** Anthony Hope **c)** Rembrandt

2. **a)** Limpopo (in *The Elephant's Child* by Rudyard Kipling) **b)** Edmund Spenser (in *Prothalamion*) **c)** Alph (in *Kubla Khan*, Samuel Taylor Coleridge)

3. *Judith Paris* (1931), *The Fortress* (1932), *Vanessa* (1933)

4. **a)** Grandfather **b)** Granddaughter **c)** Brother

5. *Chauve-souris, fledermaus, pipistrello*

6. **a)** Hanged **b)** Stabbed herself **c)** Stabbed by Iago

7. **a)** Australia **b)** Malaya **c)** China

8. **a)** Poverty *(Major Barbara)* **c)** Cynicism **c)** Rumour

9. **a)** Chocolate (brown) and cream **b)** Green **c)** Maroon

10. **a)** Sri Lanka **b)** Masada **c)** Zimbabwe

GENERAL KNOWLEDGE 11

Starters ***Answers to pages 40 and 41***

1. R L Stevenson **2.** Guglielmo Marconi **3.** The Gentleman Usher of the Black Rod **4.** Eucalyptus (leaves) **5.** Combination **6.** Black **7.** Trachoma **8.** Blarney Castle **9.** Nuremberg trials **10.** Sir Charles Kingsford-Smith **11.** John Walter **12.** Heraklion **13.** Nacre **14.** Jean-Pierre Blanchard **15.** Synthetic or aniline dyes

Bonus

1. **a)** Horse latitudes **b)** Chinook **c)** *Föhn*

2. **a)** Dirk Hatteraich **b)** *Guy Mannering* **c)** Meg Merrilies

3. **a)** Marquis de St Evrémonde **b)** Wotan **c)** Pepin III

4. **a)** France and Spain **b)** Italy and Austria **c)** Mongolia and China

5. Sir Galahad, Sir Perceval, Sir Bors

6. Cheops, Chephren, Mycerinus

7. **a)** Nell Trent **b)** Philip Pirrip **c)** Amy Dorrit

8. **a)** Marlais **b)** Lord Macaulay's **c)** Thomas (Love) Peacock

9. **a)** Type of paleolithic man **b)** Orang-utan **c)** The Pope

10. **a)** Banquo **b)** David Copperfield **c)** Augustine Washington

LITERATURE 2

Starters

Answers to pages 42 and 43

1. Tom Pearse **2.** Flodden **3.** François Rabelais **4.** Damon Runyon's (in a series of short stories) **5.** Catch 22 (in a book of the same name by Joseph Heller) **6.** Boiling in wine (White Knight in *Through the Looking-Glass*) **7.** Alexandre Federovich Kerensky **8.** Blank verse **9.** All are Belgian **10.** Anatole France **11.** Wilfred Owen **12.** Jean Arthur Rimbaud **13.** *Anatomy: of Abuses; of Melancholy; of Britain* **14.** Matthew Arnold **15.** T S Eliot *(Old Possum's Book of Cats)*

Bonus

1. **a)** J D Salinger's **b)** C P Snow's **c)** Sholem Aleichem's

2. **a)** *The Man Who was Thursday* **b)** Joe Friday **c)** Saturday Keith

3. **a)** Lolita **b)** Mellors **c)** Orlando de Boys

4. **a)** *The Age of Reason* **b)** *The Reprieve* **c)** *Iron in the Soul*

5. **a)** Sandy Wilson **b)** David Percival **c)** Oscar Wilde

6. **a)** Lilliput (in *Gulliver's Travels,* Jonathan Swift) **b)** Mr Jorrocks (in the novels of R S Surtees) **c)** Young boys employed by Sherlock Holmes

7. **a)** Mr Harding (in *The Warden*, Anthony Trollope) **b)** Sovereign Power **c)** Rienzi (in *The Last of the Tribunes* by Bulwer Lytton)

8. **a)** *Vanity Fair* (W M Thackeray) **b)** *Mary Barton* **c)** *Ben Hur*

9. **a)** John Keats's **b)** Elizabeth Barrett Browning's **c)** Shakespeare's

10. **a)** Lucy (William Wordsworth) **b)** Mary (Robert Burns) **c)** Sally (in Our Alley) (Henry Carey)

GENERAL KNOWLEDGE 12

Starters ***Answers to pages 44 and 45***

1. Boy Jack Cornwell **2.** Dr Albert Schweitzer **3.** An opera hat collapses **4.** Arabic **5.** It was the first transmitted sound of human voice over a wire (invention of the telephone) **6.** Confession of Augsburg **7.** Auguste Lumière (and his brother Louis) **8.** Spinoza **9.** *Daily Courant* **10.** A tidal wave **11.** Hasdrubal **12.** Hogmanay **13.** 9 pm **14.** Wedge-shaped **15.** François Villon

Bonus

1. **a)** Cock **b)** Wolf **c)** Badger

2. **a)** 101 **b)** 6 **c)** 8

3. **a)** Los Alamos **b)** Amarillo **c)** Las Vegas

4. **a)** *My Favourite Wife* **b)** *Philadelphia Story* **c)** *The Four Feathers*

5. **a)** Dublin **b)** Swansea **c)** Corfu

6. **a)** *Man and Superman* (Bernard Shaw) **b)** *Roots* (Arnold Wesker) **c)** *Cat on a Hot Tin Roof* (Tennessee Williams)

7. **a)** In bed **b)** In his carriage **c)** In the labyrinth

8. **a)** Annie Oakley **b)** Marie Lloyd **c)** Sir Harry Lauder

9. **a)** *451* **b)** 8 **c)** *70*

10. Sir Anthony Eden (October 1951-April 1955); Harold Macmillan (April 1955-December 1955); Selwyn Lloyd (December 1955-July 1960)

MUSIC 1

Starters

Answers to pages 46 and 47

1. Absolute pitch **2.** John Antill **3.** CEMA (Council for the Encouragement of Music and Arts, 1939) **4.** A type of zither **5.** Six **6.** Béla Bartók **7.** Thomas Bateson **8.** William Thomas Best **9.** Foxtrot **10.** System of keys on woodwind instruments **11.** 1896 (in Turin) **12.** Trombone **13.** Eighty **14.** David Garrick (the actor) **15.** Esterhazy

Bonus

1. **a)** Reed-organ **b)** Recorder **c)** Lute

2. **a)** 1912 **b)** Stuttgart **c)** Richard Strauss

3. **a)** Granville Bantock **b)** All use bells **c)** 120

4. Mily Balakiref; Alexander Borodin; César Cui; Modeste Mussorgsky; Nicholas Rimsky-Korsakof

5. **a)** Robert Schumann **b)** Felix Mendelssohn **c)** Gustav Mahler

6. **a)** Austria **b)** Belgium **c)** Eire

7. **a)** Gabriel Fauré or Jean Sibelius **b)** Claude Debussy **c)** Arnold Schoenberg

8. Daniel Auber (1856); Giacomo Puccini (1893); Jules Massenet (1884)

9. **a)** Bronze **b)** Copper **c)** Wood

10. **a)** Jerome Kern **b)** Stephen Foster **c)** George Gershwin

GENERAL KNOWLEDGE 13

Starters

Answers to pages 48 and 49

1. Glastonbury **2.** When someone is about to die **3.** Heinrich Heine **4.** A bird from Madagascar **5.** George Macaulay Trevelyan **6.** Study of fossil footprints **7.** It is the oldest-known mathematical book **8.** Battle of Adrianople in AD 378 **9.** Arthur Schopenhauer **10.** Dublin **11.** Marie Rambert **12.** Typefaces **13.** Charles Dickens **14.** Clytemnestra **15.** George Bernard Shaw

Bonus

1. a) *The Heiress* **b)** *The Wings of a Dove* **c)** *The Turn of the Screw*

2. USA (4 July); France (14 July); Cuba (20 July)

3. a) Notre Dame de la Garde **b)** Cathedral of St Vitus **c)** Cathedral of St Basil

4. a) 'Silent upon a peak in Darien' (John Keats) **b)** 'They also serve who only stand and wait' (John Milton) **c)** 'The lone and level sands stretch far away' (Percy Bysshe Shelley)

5. a) Nero's **b)** Lizzie Borden's **c)** Invention's

6. a) William III **b)** Torbay in Devon **c)** 1688

7. a) Aristotle **b)** Edmund Burke **c)** Seneca

8. a) Gold Coast **b)** Nyasaland **c)** Northern Rhodesia

9. a) Henry I **b)** John **c)** Richard I

10. a) Beverley Cross **b)** William Gibson **c)** Sir David Lyndsay

GENERAL KNOWLEDGE 14

Starters ***Answers to pages 50 and 51***

1. All have, or had, houses built on them **2.** Audie Murphy **3.** Sophocles **4.** Aurora **5.** Michael Henchard (*The Mayor of Casterbridge*) **6.** Charles II **7.** Aristotle **8.** On a shield **9.** Sodium bicarbonate **10.** Westminster Hall **11.** Dionysius **12.** Benjamin Disraeli **13.** Hernando Cortés **14.** Merlin **15.** Bloody Cranesbill

Bonus

1. **a)** Hector **b)** Menelaus **c)** Priam

2. **a)** Captain **b)** Rear-admiral **c)** Superintendent

3. **a)** Hurricane **b)** Cyclone **c)** Typhoon

4. **a)** *Through the Looking-Glass* (Lewis Carroll) **b)** *Checkmate* (Sir Arthur Bliss) **c)** *The Seventh Seal* (Ingmar Bergman)

5. **a)** Windward Islands **b)** Orkneys **c)** Channel Islands

6. **a)** Spree **b)** Rio de la Plata **c)** Ganges

7. **a)** Lily Langtry **b)** Catherine Parr **c)** Rita Hayworth

8, **a)** Walter Scott **b)** Alphonse Daudet **c)** Prosper Mérimée

9. *Widowers' Houses; The Philanderer; Mrs Warren's Profession*

10. **a)** Cambridge **b)** Leningrad **c)** Amsterdam

MUSIC 2

Starters

Answers to pages 52 and 53

1. Mrs Cecil Frances Alexander **2.** Joseph Haydn **3.** Apollo **4.** Wolfgang Amadeus Mozart **5.** With the mute **6.** Edvard Grieg's **7.** Czech **8.** Arthur Honegger **9.** Castell Sant'Angelo **10.** François Poulenc **11.** *Patience* **12.** Claude Rouget de Lisle **13.** Hector Berlioz **14.** *Bluebeard's Castle* **15.** Frederick Smetana

Bonus

1. **a)** Joseph Haydn **b)** Wolfgang Amadeus Mozart **c)** Ernest Bloch

2. **a)** Arpeggione **b)** Cymbalom **c)** Spinet

3. **a)** William Walton **b)** Domenico Scarlatti's **c)** Arthur Sullivan arr. Charles Mackerras

4. **a)** Sir Arthur Bliss **b)** *The Olympians* **c)** *Miracle in the Gorbals*

5. **a)** Samuel Coleridge Taylor **b)** *Aida* **c)** Rossini

6. **a)** Creating a song in *Die Meistersinger* **b)** He used magic bullets **c)** *Cosi Fan Tutte* (Mozart)

7. **a)** Joseph Haydn **b)** William Walton **c)** George Frederick Handel

8. **a)** 'The Bear' **b)** Domenico Scarlatti's **c)** Frédéric Chopin

9. **a)** Florrie Forde **b)** *Semele* **c)** Pete Seeger

GENERAL KNOWLEDGE 15

Starters ***Answers to pages 54 and 55***

1. Geography **2.** Charterhouse **3.** Barbara Hepworth **4.** Roald Amundsen **5.** El Cid **6.** Propertius Sextus **7.** Liberia **8.** Auberon Waugh **9.** Lamb **10.** Cleopatra's Needle **11.** Cordite **12.** Helium **13.** Viscosity **14.** Abbreviation for navigator **15.** Mandrake

Bonus

1. **a)** William Empson **b)** T E Lawrence **c)** Aeschylus

2. **a)** Imogen *(Cymbeline)* **b)** Bellerophon **c)** 'Three Jolly Gentlemen' (Walter de la Mare)

3. **a)** *The Tale of Mr Jeremy Fisher* (French) **b)** *The Tale of Mrs Tiggy-Winkle* (Welsh) **c)** *The Tale of Peter Rabbit* (Latin)

4. **a)** Private Act of Parliament **b)** Archbishop Cranmer **c)** Sir Alan P Herbert

5. **a)** Garden of Hesperides **b)** Apollo **c)** Eurystheus

6. **a)** Lord Darnley's **b)** Lord Bothwell **c)** James, 4th Earl of Morton

7. **a)** La Pléiade **b)** Group of seven tragic Greek poets of the 3rd century BC **c)** Star cluster Pleiades

8. **a)** Bamburgh Castle **b)** Whin Sill **c)** Grace Darling

9. **a)** The Great Cham **b)** Earl of Chatham **c)** William III

10. **a)** Rob Roy **b)** Ned Kelly **c)** Robin Hood

MYTHOLOGY AND ANCIENT HISTORY

Starters

Answers to pages 56 and 57

1. Daedalus (builder of the maze for Minos) **2.** Jocasta (his mother) **3.** The Pharos **4.** Poseidon **5.** Pheasant **6.** Halicarnassus **7.** *Flying Dutchman* **8.** Ichór **9.** Delos **10.** Vespasian **11.** The main sewer of Ancient Rome **12.** Alberich **13.** Griffin **14.** Hippolytes **15.** Lucifer

Bonus

1. **a)** Jason **b)** Perseus **c)** Theseus

2. **a)** Sicily **b)** Gogmagog **c)** Brobdingnagians

3. **a)** The Three Graces **b)** The Rhine-maidens **c)** The dogs that King Lear thought were barking at him

4. **a)** A smith **b)** Siegfried **c)** Hephaestus

5. **a)** It was full of ashes **b)** Tomato **c)** Aphrodite (Venus)

6. **a)** Gloucester. **b)** St Albans **c)** Chester

7. **a)** Paris **b)** Lyons **c)** Leyden

8. **a)** Atropos **b)** Clotho **c)** Lachesis

9. **a)** Romulus and Remus **b)** Castor and Pollux **c)** Hercules (Heracles)

10. **a)** Queen Guinevere (with Mordred) **b)** Iseult **c)** Dido

GENERAL KNOWLEDGE 16

Starters

Answers to pages 58 and 59

1. That Francis Bacon wrote Shakespeare's plays **2.** William Shakespeare **3.** Onion **4.** Representation of the winding of bandage around an arm before blood-letting **5.** Extra-Sensory Perception **6.** Red **7.** Quicksilver **8.** FIDO (Fog Intensive Dispersal Operation) **9.** Laughing gas **10.** Hermann Goering **11.** Borstal **12.** To make objections to a claim for canonisation **13.** Langdale Pikes **14.** Migraine **15.** Mole (*The Wind in the Willows* by Kenneth Grahame)

Bonus

1. **a)** Arctic fern **b)** Painted Lady **c)** Seals
2. **a)** Sinope **b)** Diogenes **c)** Mithridates VI
3. **a)** Hadrian **b)** Alexander **c)** Beddgelert
4. **a)** Congress of Vienna (1815) **b)** Belgium **c)** USA
5. **a)** Blood poisoning **b)** Marsh fever **c)** Elizabeth Barrett Browning
6. **a)** October (25th 1854) **b)** June (18th 1815) **c)** April (16th 1746)
7. **a)** Golden House of Nero **b)** Soames Forsyte **c)** Theobalds (near Waltham Cross)
8. **a)** Boadicea **b)** Ben Hur **c)** Phaethon (son of Helios)
9. **a)** To murder the British Cabinet in 1820 **b)** To release Mary Queen of Scots and restore papal authority **c)** To murder Charles II
10. **a)** Friedrich Froebel **b)** Maria Montessori **c)** Transvaal, South Africa

GENERAL KNOWLEDGE 17

Starters

Answers to pages 60 and 61

1. Boiling point **2.** Unit of mass (used by aeronautical engineers) **3.** Head of a ram **4.** Lyonnesse **5.** Monitor **6.** Lady Astor **7.** Condition of being a dwarf **8.** 1746 **9.** A wisp **10.** Benjamin Constant (*Journal Intime,* 1804) **11.** Louis VI **12.** John Knox **13.** Meander **14.** *Deo Optimo Maximo* (To God the best and the greatest) **15.** 1928

Bonus

1. **a)** Lord George Murray **b)** Sir John Cope **c)** Derby

2. **a)** A J Balfour **b)** Bonar Law **c)** Stanley Baldwin

3. **a)** A Greek **b)** A Jew **c)** A member of a Germanic tribe

4. **a)** Stabiae (Castellamare) **b)** Stromboli **c)** USA (Alaska)

5. **a)** Giovanni Bernini **b)** St Theresa **c)** Fountains

6. **a)** Doric **b)** Ionic **c)** British Museum (part of the Elgin Marbles)

7. **a)** Honours **b)** Fake Vermeer paintings **c)** Panama Canal

8. **a)** Ruby **b)** Aquamarine **c)** Emerald

9. **a)** Bridewell **b)** Newgate **c)** The Clink

10. **a)** Tyre **b)** Lebanon **c)** Lucan

RELIGIONS

Starters

Answers to pages 62 and 63

1. Dead Sea (Lot's wife) **2.** The Magi **3.** A shepherd **4.** Every ten years **5.** Nebuchadnezzar **6.** St Mark's **7.** The death of Moses **8.** Zipporah **9.** Abraham's (Hagar) **10.** The land of Shinar **11.** Abracadabra **12.** The Assassins **13.** Dietrich Bonhoeffer **14.** The election of a new pope **15.** Hugh of Lincoln

Bonus

1. **a)** Constantine the Great **b)** St Bernadette of Lourdes **c)** King Andrew II of Hungary

2. **a)** August (1) **b)** November (11) **c)** September (29)

3. **a)** Death of Saul and Jonathan at Gilboa **b)** David **c)** Job

4. **a)** Aaron **b)** Jeroboam **c)** To regulate the election and coronation of an emperor

5. **a)** Deuteronomy **b)** Joshua **c)** Ruth

6. **a)** Ur of the Chaldees **b)** Gath **c)** Bethlehem

7. **a)** The Kingdom of Heaven **b)** To see God **c)** To be called the Children of God

8. **a)** Solomon **b)** Balaam **c)** Prophet Elisha

9. **a)** Seven **b)** Ephesus; Smyrna; Pergamum; Thyatira; Sardis; Philadelphia; Laodicea

10. **a)** Shinto **b)** The Aga Khan **c)** Moderator

GENERAL KNOWLEDGE 18

Starters ***Answers to pages 64 and 65***

1. Dr. Johnson's *Dictionary* **2.** Margaret Bondfield (1929—31, Minister of Labour) **3.** Baron Munchausen **4.** Sir Charles Barry **5.** Number of horned cattle owned by a servant **6.** Poseidon **7.** 1348 **8.** Action painting **9.** Mount Vernon **10.** Armour **11.** Albert Einstein **12.** Galvanising **13.** Halifax **14.** Thermodynamics **15.** Mistinguett

Bonus

1. **a)** Dale Carnegie **b)** J McNeill Whistler **c)** George Fox

2. **a)** Italy **b)** Gotham **c)** New York

3. **a)** Al Capone **b)** St Bartholomew's Massacre **c)** St Peter's Fields, Manchester (Peterloo)

4. Le Notre; Le Brun; Le Vau

5. **a)** Cerberus **b)** Orion's **c)** Lassie

6. **a)** Day of Atonement **b)** Purification of the Virgin Mary (2 February) **c)** Sowing of crops (December)

7. **a)** Benedictus de Spinoza **b)** René Descartes **c)** Spanish Jews who had to become Christians during the Inquisition

8. **a)** Elephants **b)** Having a long nose **c)** Spiny anteater (Echidna)

9. Sir Thomas Lawrence; George Romney; Thomas Gainsborough

10. **a)** Samuel Johnson **b)** David Garrick **c)** *The Rambler*

SCIENCE

Starters

Answers to pages 66 and 67

1. Calamine **2.** In an aquarium or fish tank **3.** Proconsul **4.** Zinc **5.** Meteorites **6.** A form of zircon (cut as a gemstone) **7.** Sheffield plate **8.** Ozone **9.** A L Lavoisier **10.** Ivy **11.** They form pumice **12.** Funny bone **13.** A foxglove **14.** —40° (minus forty degrees) **15.** Arthur H Compton

Bonus

1. **a)** Kinematics **b)** Kinetic **c)** Dynamics

2. **a)** Pancreas **b)** Spleen **c)** Liver

3. Sweet; salty; sour; bitter

4. **a)** Tuberculosis **b)** Bacille (Bacillus) Calmette Guérin

5. Iron; nickel; carbon

6. **a)** Prussic acid **b)** K W Scheele **c)** Prussian blue (potassium ferric ferricyanide)

7. **a)** Dmitri Mendeleyev **b)** Lothar Meyer **c)** Sir Joseph James Thomson

8. **a)** Crystal **b)** Bloodstone **c)** Onyx

9. **a)** Aluminium **b)** Iron **c)** Lead

10. **a)** Second vertebra in the neck **b)** Breastbone **c)** Shinbone

GENERAL KNOWLEDGE 19

Starters

Answers to pages 68 and 69

1. Alfred Noyes **2.** Oxford Street **3.** Alfred de Vigny **4.** Valet **5.** Canada **6.** On the floor of the North Atlantic Ocean **7.** Platinum (the six platinum metals) **8.** Thomas de Quincey **9.** That the car was made in or before 1933 (the year in which Royce died) **10.** Meerschaum **11.** The Queen's Gallery at Buckingham Palace **12.** W T Sherman **13.** Aaron **14.** Emily Davies **15.** Dardanelles

Bonus

1. **a)** St Martin **b)** St Francis of Assisi **c)** One of the soldiers at the Crucifixion

2. Republic of Venice; Republic of Florence; Duchy of Milan; Papal States; Kingdom of Naples

3. **a)** China **b)** Nehru **c)** Chou En-lai

4. **a)** King Edward II's **b)** Gawain **c)** Gilgamesh's

5. **a)** Claudius Ptolemy **b)** Nicolaus Copernicus **c)** John Napier

6. **a)** Sporades **b)** Tonga **c)** France

7. *Phineas Redux; The Prime Minister; The Duke's Children*

8. **a)** Hare **b)** Fish **c)** Monotremata

9. **a)** Compton Mackenzie **b)** John Steinbeck **c)** Somerset Maugham

10. **a)** The Wailing Wall **b)** The Antonine Wall **c)** Wall Street

GENERAL KNOWLEDGE 20

Starters

Answers to pages 70 and 71

1. Evelyn John Strachey **2.** 1803 **3.** Copper, zinc and tin **4.** Cardinal Newman **5.** Fray Bentos **6.** India **7.** Roland, the narrator's horse **8.** Regent's Circus **9.** Sylvite **10.** John Adams (November 1800) **11.** *Death in Venice* **12.** The heroine of a book by Max Beerbohm **13.** None **14.** Slaying the Nemean Lion **15.** Different types of helmet

Bonus

1. **a)** Canaan **b)** Samson **c)** Alexander

2. **a)** Cain **b)** A rib **c)** Eve

3. **a)** Marie Antoinette **b)** Elizabeth Taylor **c)** De Beer's

4. **a)** A pipe **b)** A cat **c)** A looking glass

5. **a)** Oliver Cromwell **b)** Sainthood **c)** Easter Sunday

6. **a)** A tail **b)** The Père David sheds them twice a year **c)** They have only four toes on each foot

7. **a)** *Oliver Twist* **b)** *A Tale of Two Cities* **c)** *Great Expectations*

8. **a)** Richard Steele and Joseph Addison **b)** The Hanoverian succession **c)** Political differences

9. Chile; Peru; Ecuador; Colombia; Panama

10. **a)** Pharoah **b)** Siegmund Freud's **c)** At Wuthering Heights (in the book of the same name by Emily Brontë)

SPORTS AND PASTIMES

Starters

Answers to pages 72 and 73

1. Basketball **2.** Polo **3.** Grand National Course at Aintree **4.** The bull in bullfighting **5.** Nap (Napoleon)—a card game **6.** QR 4 (names for squares on chess board from each end) **7.** Edmund Hoyle's **8.** 200 yards **9.** Emil Zatopek (Czechoslovakia) (1952, Helsinki) **10.** Cribbage **11.** 1964 (Tokyo) **12.** After taking three wickets with consecutive balls **13.** The King's Cup (presented by George V) **14.** King of Diamonds **15.** *Sha-mat*: the king is dead (Arabic)

Bonus

1. **a)** Cycling (Roy Booty) **b)** John Landy **c)** 7 feet
2. **a)** The rest of Europe (except Russia) **b)** George Hardwick **c)** Great Britain 6-1
3. **a)** Lacrosse **b)** Real tennis **c)** Bowls
4. **a)** 1956 (10 March) **b)** Lionel Peter Twiss **c)** Fairey Delta 2
5. **a)** Blue **b)** Red **c)** White
6. **a)** Doncaster **b)** Epsom **c)** Newmarket
7. **a)** Goodison Park **b)** Hillsborough **c)** Anfield
8. **a)** 1896 **b)** 1905 **c)** 10.6 seconds
9. **a)** *Jeu de paume* **b)** Sphairistike **c)** Marylebone Cricket Club
10. **a)** 1787 **b)** 1814 **c)** J T Bosanquet

GENERAL KNOWLEDGE 21

Starters

Answers to pages 74 and 75

1. *The Hunting of the Snark* (Lewis Carroll) **2.** Thirteen **3.** El Greco **4.** All are species of butterfly **5.** Richard I **6.** O'Hara **7.** Murder **8.** Benjamin Britten **9.** Denmark **10.** Puck or Robin Goodfellow **11.** Levi **12.** 1917 **13.** A total abstainer **14.** Sarah Bernhardt **15.** American (Robert Peary)

Bonus

1. a) John Bunyan's **b)** Muhammed Ali's (Cassius Clay) **c)** Giovanni Boccaccio's

2. a) Overland expedition from St Louis to the Pacific and back **b)** Australia **c)** Source of the Nile

3. a) George Stephenson **b)** Liverpool and Manchester Railway Company **c)** Richard Trevithick

4. a) Jupiter **b)** Its great red spot **c)** Four

5. a) Jonah **b)** Gadarene **c)** 150 days

6. a) 1588 (The Armada) **b)** 1653 (Dissolution of the Long Parliament) **c)** 1757 (The Condemnation of Byng)

7. a) The Horae **b)** The Hesperides (The nymphs of the west) **c)** The Graiae (the Grey Ones)

8. a) Pass of Thermopylae (480 BC) **b)** Cocles (Horatius) **c)** Siraj-ud-Daulah

9. a) The Senne **b)** Manneken-Pis (statue of small boy) **c)** Willebroek

THEATRE AND CINEMA

Starters

Answers to pages 76 and 77

1. Harold Pinter **2.** Phineas T Barnum **3.** Michelangelo Antonioni **4.** Sherlock Holmes **5.** The Marx Brothers (*A Night in Casablanca, A Night at the Opera, A Day at the Races*) **6.** Joe Orton **7.** John Boynton Priestley **8.** NO SMOKING (Nosmo King) **9.** *Le Malade Imaginaire* **10.** *Gone with the Wind* **11.** Adelina Patti **12.** At Tiffany's **13.** Edmund Kean **14.** Pandarus **15.** Nell Gwynne

Bonus

1. **a)** Arthur Miller **b)** Clark Gable **c)** John Huston

2. **a)** Brutus **b)** Cassius **c)** Battlefield of Philippi

3. **a)** Russia **b)** *The Jazz Singer* **c)** Larry Parkes

4. **a)** Water skiing **b)** Rugby League **c)** Surfing

5. **a)** Mistress Ford and Mistress Page **b)** Hermione and Leontes' son (*The Winter's Tale*) **c)** *Measure for Measure*

6. **a)** Constable (*Much Ado About Nothing*) **b)** Tinker (*The Taming of the Shrew*) **c)** Parson (*The Merry Wives of Windsor*)

7. **a)** Princess Ida **b)** The Major-General (*The Pirates of Penzance*) **c)** John Wellington Wells (*The Sorcerer*)

8. **a)** Seville **b)** Molière **c)** *Man and Superman*

9. **a)** *Juno and the Paycock* (Sean O'Casey) **b)** *Death of a Salesman* (Arthur Miller) **c)** *The Family Reunion* (T S Eliot)

10. **a)** French **b)** Vicar **c)** A clown